P U Z Z L E W I S E ™

A simple step-by-step year-round program to augment your current lessons so public, private, and home school students develop into knowledgeable, independent self-motivated life-long learners

GOALS

- Greatly increase students' state mandated math test scores
- Increase parental involvement
- Double school-home communication
- Increase enjoyable grade-level math activities outside of school

PUZZLE BUDDY CONTACT

Please write the name of your Puzzle Buddies and their relationships to you here:

Name: 1. _____   2. _____
Relationship: 1. _____   2. _____

PARENT CONTRACT

Dear Parents and Guardians,

This school year we request that you support your child's learning by ensuring your child completes at least one lesson in this book each week. Every _____ your child should bring his/her puzzle book to school so the teacher can review the completed work and check progress. Please check the statements below that work for your family, and sign this contract showing your support for this program.

☐ I have read the Helpful Hints for parents on page 15, and will follow those that make sense for our family.

☐ I will make sure my child takes his/her puzzle book to school on the scheduled day.

☐ I will monitor my child's progress on a regular basis, encouraging him/her to keep up with the weekly schedule.

☐ I understand that my child does not have to finish the puzzle homework assignments. It's more important that my child tries hard, because success is often achieved with steady steps over time.

☐ I will consider buying a copy of this book for myself so I can improve my math skills and be more help for my child in the higher grades.

☐ I will notify my child's teacher if my child experiences repetitive frustration.

☐ I will help my child see that working on these crossword puzzles is fun and purposeful.

☐ I will help my child find a safe place in our home where this book can be kept. I will notify the teacher if my child loses or misplaces this PuzzleWise™ book.

I agree to the statements that I have checked above.

_____   _____
Parent/Guardian Signature   Date

Track Assessment Progress

$(7/10 = 70\%)$

5	/ =	%
10	/ =	%
15	/ =	%
20	/ =	%
25	/ =	%
30	/ =	%
35	/ =	%
40	/ =	%
45	/ =	%

PUZZLEWISE™

MATH

Level 5

36 Weekly Lessons and 9 Monthly Assessments

Math Skill and Math Literacy Practice
Aligned with National and State Mathematics Learning
Standards and Assessments

Dr. Daniel Levine and Matt W. Beck, Founders
Copyright ©2006 by Test Best International, Incorporated™

August 2006

Fourth Edition

TO ORDER, PLEASE CONTACT:
Puzzlewise™
P.O. Box 28312
Bellingham, WA 98228 U.S.A.
1-360-650-0671
Fax 1-866-683-3219
www.puzzlewise.com
daniellevine@puzzlewise.com
mattbeck@puzzlewise.com

Contributing Authors

DR. MICHAEL NAYLOR (*Author: Math Puzzles*) is an outstanding math educator, international presenter, and national columnist. Dr. Naylor has taught mathematics to students of all ages for over 12 years, and is the author of the "Teaching Math" column for *Teaching K-8* Magazine. Dr. Naylor is also an associate professor of Mathematics and Mathematics Education specializing in K-8 math education. Michael's highly acclaimed seminars and workshops generate excitement for mathematics and have captured audiences imaginations across the U.S., Canada, Europe and Africa. Michael is also the author of numerous children's books and publications in popular mathematics. "I developed this series of books after analyzing and comparing state and national mathematics expectations for children. The math questions target specific grade level standards and develop problem solving skills students need for success on state standardized tests. The questions are fun and challenging, and build students' vocabulary, computation, and math literacy skills. PuzzleWise™ is an exciting way to reach children!"

ROXANN ROSE (*Author: Teacher and Parent Guides*) is an innovative teacher, national presenter, and respected educational consultant. Ms. Rose taught elementary students in three different states, on both coasts of the United States for 11 years. Roxann was recognized for her innovative and effective teaching strategies in 1996 when the Walt Disney Company honored her dedication to her students. She was one of 36 teachers chosen nationwide to be honored by Disney's American Teacher Awards. Roxann's teaching is highlighted in Harvard Project Zero's Creative Teaching Video Series. She continues to work with Disney Learning Partnership to recognize stellar teachers across the United States. Roxann teaches future teachers and works with current teachers to help them reflect on and improve their teaching practices. "I agree with Michael: PuzzleWise™ is an exceptional learning tool. Students will be excited, parents will be appreciative, and teachers will be relieved."

We and other educational experts feel that the following PuzzleWise elements are critical for success on state tests and also promote the love of learning:

1. **Spiral Learning** — Visiting and revisiting mathematical strands such as number sense, measurement, geometry, algebra, probability and vocabulary for math all year long.

2. **Differentiation** — Allow students to work at their own level and speed, developing organically.

3. **On-going Assessment** — Monitor student growth consistently, starting in the first grade. You'll be able to easily track your students' test readiness every year, focusing on such critical elements as their degree of scholastic effort, problem-solving strategies, critical thinking, logical reasoning, and communicating their understanding — all of which are critical for success on the state tests.

4. **High Expectations** — "If you think you can or can't, you are right." It's only by believing in a student's ultimate success that success can be achieved.

5. **Alignment with Grade Level Expectation** — Reach benchmarks and maintain continuity.

6. **Problem Solving** — Students learn concepts and operations best when they're actively finding their own solutions to interesting problems.

7. **Resources Outside School** — Children are at school only 13% of the school year. Helping students find a parent, older sibling, grandparent, or friend to assist them not only builds a significant relationship, but also supplies the personal resource they need for math success.

8. **Year-long Test Practice** — The more familiar students can become with the type of problems they'll encounter, the more success they'll have on the actual tests.

9. **Fun** — People learn best when they play. Life-long learners always have fun when they learn.

10. **Success Starts in the First Grade** — This is the ideal time for students to adopt the key elements of success! Otherwise, success becomes harder to achieve with each passing year.

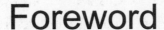

Foreword

We are pleased to present this exceptional book of Level 5 math activities providing students with the regular practice needed for the state tests. Each individual lesson is directly linked to the state and national fifth grade math skill expectations. PuzzleWise™ books meet all ten of the national math standards, regarded as the core of state grade level expectations (GLEs) for every state in the U.S.A.

Students need to become self-motivated, year-round, life-long learners. These activities build a foundation for the enjoyment of mental challenges, and inspire the love for a lifetime of continued learning. By doing these activities and playing as they learn, students build a life-long habit as independent self-motivated learners, acquire the required state math skills, increase math engagement by 30%, and create improved personal value as they prepare for successful and productive lives.

In addition to being a fun way of learning and practicing the necessary math skills and vocabulary required by the state tests, PuzzleWise™ books are crafted to help students achieve the **Seven Essential Student Learnings**:

Knowledgeable Individuals
Quality Producers
Effective Communicators
Competent Thinkers
Effective Collaborators
Responsible Citizens
Life-Long Learners.

Furthermore, Lessons 1-10 are a blend of level four and level five material, allowing early success for students as the new school year begins and the need for refresher activities is paramount. Also, Lessons 41-45 represent a blend of level five and level six materials to challenge students with a new level of perspective and expectations. You'll also note that the puzzle clues are staggered with fewer clues in the beginning puzzles, increasing as the student matures.

The answer keys in the back of the book allow students to self-correct their work and limit the amount of correcting required of teachers already sufficiently burdened. However, to help teachers retain control of the answer keys, every fifth key is on the last page of this book, providing the opportunity to remove the page with scissors and keep these nine puzzles for teacher-directed assessment.

Our books can be used in many different ways to suit your class requirements. Students needing remediation can be assisted by choosing the level of the book to fit their skills, or with the word lists we provide on our Web site. The word lists are provided separately so you can choose how, or whether, to incorporate them into your teaching program. In addition, our books can be incorporated into a summer transition program. We always ask students to read but seldom offer good math material for summer vacation.

Best regards,

Dr. Daniel Levine & Mr. Matt Beck

About The Founders: Dr. Levine is a Doctor of Education, was a teacher for nine years, and a superintendent for 16 years.

Mr. Beck has a Masters in Education, served 20 years as a teacher, has created three non-profit foundations, and is a certificated school administrator.

New Books From PuzzleWise™

Supplemental programs for regular, gifted, remedial and ELL students
Grades 1–8

Testimonial:

"I am convinced these books have a positive impact on their reasoning, problem-solving abilities and knowledge. I know they are helping me prepare my students for their future."
—Jane Robertson, Arizona Teacher of the Year, 2004.

Innovative Ways to Use Our Books:

We have several new options to help you incorporate our books into your teaching program, in the way best suited to helping *your* students.

• **See the listed applications on page 14.**

• **For additional remediation,** we offer word lists for every puzzle on our Web site. You choose when to offer word lists, depending on the needs of your students.

• You can also use our books in a **summer enrichment program**. If you plan your schedule so that sufficient puzzles remain to be completed over the summer, our math books can double as your summer transition materials!

Visit
www.PuzzleWise.com

• Download free sample puzzles!
• Order books!

Thank you!

Dr. Daniel Levine
1-360-650-0671
Fax 1-866-683-3219
daniellevine@puzzlewise.com

PUZZLEWISE™

National Content Standards in PuzzleWise Books

Visit our Web site for more information about the national standards.

		1	2	3	4	5	6	7	8	9	10	11	12
Number & Operations	Understand numbers, ways of representing numbers, relationships among numbers, and number systems	●	●	●	●	●	●	●	●				
	Understand meanings of operations and how they relate to one another	●	●	●	●	●	●	●	●				
	Compute fluently and make reasonable estimates	●	●	●	●	●	●	●	●				
Measurement	Understand measurable attributes of objects and the units, systems, and processes of measurement	●	●	●	●	●	●	●	●				
	Apply appropriate techniques, tools, and formulas to determine measurements	●	●	●	●	●	●	●	●				
Geometry	Analyze characteristics and properties of two-and three-dimensional geometric shapes and develop mathematical arguments about geometric relationships	●	●	●	●	●	●	●	●				
	Specify locations and describe spatial relationships using coordinate geometry and other representational systems		●	●	●	●	●	●	●				
	Apply transformations and use symmetry to analyze mathematical situations	●	●	●	●	●	●	●	●				
	Use visualization, spatial reasoning, and geometric modeling to solve problems	●	●	●	●	●	●	●	●				
Data Analysis & Probability	Formulate questions addressing data and collect, organize, and display relevant data to answer them	●	●	●	●	●	●	●	●				
	Select and use appropriate statistical methods to analyze data		●	●	●	●	●	●	●				
	Develop and evaluate inferences and predictions that are based on data	●	●	●	●	●	●	●	●				
	Understand and apply basic concepts of probability		●	●	●	●	●	●	●				
Algebraic Reasoning	Understand patterns, relations and functions	●	●	●	●	●	●	●	●				
	Represent and analyze mathematical situations and structures using algebraic symbols	●	●	●	●	●	●	●	●				
	Use mathematical models to represent and understand quantitative relationships	●	●	●	●	●	●	●	●				
	Analyze change in various contexts		●	●	●	●	●	●	●				

PuzzleWise™ Books Coming Soon!

(This product has not been reviewed or endorsed by the NCTM (National Council of Teachers of Mathematics). The NCTM does not endorse any product.)

Successful Strategies for Answering State Test Questions

To be successful on state tests, students must be proficient in all five national content strands *and* they must be able to use these skills to: • reason • solve problems • represent situations • make connections • and communicate.

In these puzzles, students are building these critical skills and putting them to use on the test question pages. The multiple choice and the written response questions have their own strategies which students should know and use. These strategies will help your students' mathematical development as well as achieve higher scores.

General Strategies:

90 Multiple Choice Questions
- **Estimate** the answer – which answer choices are closest?
- **Eliminate** obviously wrong choices.
- **Work backwards** from choices to see which answers make sense.

45 Written Response Questions
- Practice the **3-step plan**.
- Discuss and name **specific strategies**.

Problem Solving Strategies:

There are as many ways to think about a problem as there are minds working on it, but there is one general method for problem solving that helps students focus their thinking. Introduce the plan and use it as a structure both for solving problems and for discussing strategies. Students who regularly practice problem solving can excel on state tests.

Preparation: Show the 3-Step Plan or make a poster of it, then use the model with your class. Have your students get in the habit of using the plan while working on problems.

3-Step Plan for Problem Solving

1. **Understand the Problem.** Put the problem in your own words.

2. **Plan a Solution.** Is this a good problem to...
   - draw a picture?
   - guess and check?
   - try numbers?
   - work backwards?
   - make a table?
   - draw a graph?

   Try **many** different strategies – which ones worked and which ones didn't?

3. **Answer and Look Back.** Answer the question clearly. Reread the question to be sure you've answered it completely.

   - Ask yourself, "Does the answer make sense?"
   - Reread the question. Have you answered it completely?
   - Is your answer clear? Is it easy for someone else to understand?
   - Did you include appropriate units?

Review: Structure the discussion around the 3-Step Plan. Ask one or two students to restate the problem and then ask students for different answers and methods. Every problem can be solved many different ways and the more ways students hear from their peers, the more flexibility they'll have in solving problems. It's important to hear about strategies that didn't work as well!

During discussion **keep the focus on successful strategies**. Give the strategies **names** like "Guess and Check" for general strategies or invented names for students' inventions, such as "Maggie's Rectangle Strategy" or "Peter's Regrouping Method". Make a poster of strategy names and add to it during the year. This will not only create a feeling of classroom ownership of the mathematics, but it will also make the strategies easy to reference, and easy to recall for use on other problems, ultimately making your students flexible thinkers and successful test-takers.

PUZZLEWISE™

Abridged Guide for Teachers and Parents

1. Sessions 1-3: CLASSWORK. Don't give out books yet!

• Do the first three puzzles as a class.

• Give each student a photocopy of the clues WITHOUT the puzzle grid.

• Put the grid on an overhead display.

2. Sessions 4-6: SMALL GROUPS. Hand out books. Redo first three puzzles.

• Introduce books and resources.

• Students work in groups of 2 or 3.

• Students rework puzzles 1-3.

• Collect the books.

3. Remainder of the Year: WORK AT HOME. Assign one lesson per week.

• Distribute the books.

• Students work with a puzzle buddy at home.

• Discuss for 30 minutes each week in class.

• Every 5th puzzle is an assessment.

4. Read the following guide for teachers and parents in its entirety to understand the details of this program and to ensure student success.

Guide for Teachers and Parents

"Whether you believe you can do a thing or not, you are right."
Henry Ford, Automobile Industry Leader

Our Vision: Every child is a knowledgeable, independent, self-motivated life-long learner.

PRE-TEACHING ACTIVITIES:

• Read the Parent Contract, the Foreword, About the Authors, and the Helpful Hints pages.
• Review this Guide for Teachers and Parents in its entirety.
• Make a copy of Lesson 1, and work it yourself so you get a feel for the activity.
• Review the entire book quickly so you know how it's laid out.
• Consider cutting out the last page of every student book so the assessment answer keys are restricted.
• Reminder: if any students require additional remediation, word banks for each individual crossword puzzle are available from our Web site.

ANNUAL SCHEDULE:

Most teachers opt to use the home practice program, which they initiate in their classroom. If you choose to use this model, the biggest time commitment is only in the first four classroom hours, during which you provide the foundation for your students' success in content skills and life-long learning.

Note: Any step can be expanded or diminished at the teacher's discretion!

1 | STEP 1: Class sessions 1 – 3: (Whole class activity):

GOALS:

1. Students learn research skills.

2. Students develop critical-thinking skills and problem-solving strategies.

3. Students are introduced to math content grade level expectations.

• This step introduces the genre of crossword puzzles, and allows you to teach researching, problem-solving, and critical thinking skills so your students can become knowledgeable independent learners.

• **Do not distribute the puzzle books.** (Wait for Step 2. Also, you have permission to photocopy the following:)

• We recommend making an overhead transparency of Lesson 1's crossword puzzle, but of the grid sections only. Also, photocopy Lesson 1's crossword clues and distribute to your students. Since students only have the clues, they'll have to watch the grid transparency on the overhead. They won't be distracted and you'll maintain their full attention as you teach.

• Start with any clue, and teach your students how to work a crossword puzzle, solve unfamiliar problems, and use resources to acquire solutions (textbooks, dictionaries, ruler…). Work the clues together, as a class.

• Use modeling to solve unfamiliar problems; it's the critical key to success! Show students how to solve problems using resources, words, numbers and pictures.

• Remember to use these four steps when introducing a new concept to your students:

　1. Have a student read the problem aloud.

　2. Ask if anyone in the class can solve the problem. Provide adequate wait time.

　3. Have the student explain how they solved the problem, or teacher explains.

　4. Offer other examples of the same type of problem if needed.

• Some classes need to spend only one or two class sessions on Step 1, and some need more. Also, if your students need more practice, use the Lesson 2 (and Lesson 3) crossword puzzle. You decide when to advance your class to Step 2.

STEP 2: Class sessions 4 – 6: (In-class independent or small group activity):

GOALS:

1. Students effectively communicate their understanding of mathematics.
2. Students share strategies with their peers.
3. Students work toward independence such as reasoning logically and making connections.

- This step helps students achieve success at working toward independence by doing the same lessons (Lessons 1-3) individually or in pairs that they previously did as part of a large group.

- Dedicate 30 minutes a day of class time.

- Distribute the books. (Collect them at the end of each class.)

- Have students write both their name and their teacher's name on the inside front cover.

- Have students work on Lesson 1 on their own or in small groups. As this is a lesson they've already done as a class activity, it should be familiar and proceed easily.

- Stop work periodically to review, as a class. Ask the group to choose 2-3 problems with which students need assistance. This is an opportunity for a great teaching moment!

- Follow the four "new concept" steps, listed above in Step 1.

- After your students have done Lesson 1, advance to Lesson 2, etc., doing the lessons individually or in small groups. Some classes need to spend only a few class sessions on Step 2, and some need more. You decide when to advance your class to Step 3.

REMEMBER: Any step can be expanded or diminished at the teacher's discretion!

STEP 3: Remainder Of The School Year (Weekly home assignments):

GOALS:

1. Students enlist the support of a math helper (Puzzle Buddy).
2. Students practice and mature their scholastic independence.
3. Students build their knowledge base by steadily visiting/revisiting concepts.
4. The teacher's instruction is enhanced by spiral learning of the five content strands.
5. Students practice the five process strands and develop test-taking skills.

- Students are now ready to be independent learners, with emphasis on work-at-home. Students can take their books home!

- Assign students to identify 1-2 people outside school to be their "Puzzle Buddy." A Puzzle Buddy can be a parent, guardian, grandparent, other older relative, friend or neighbor. This person is a resource to assist them with clues.

- Students write the name(s) and relationship of their Puzzle Buddy on the inside front cover. During the year, students are encouraged to do their lessons with their Puzzle Buddy as a fun way of learning, and solving challenging problems. Their Puzzle Buddy becomes the main resource person.

- This is where the 36 weekly assignments begin. Students are to complete one lesson a week, on their own. Students write the due date in the space at the bottom of each page. Use your planning book and/or class calendar to remind students about the lessons to be completed each week, and to remind yourself about the

- Students bring in their books once a week for a 30-minute in-class activity time ("puzzle time") so the teacher can observe student progress and facilitate student peer-to-peer communication, critical thinking, and problem-solving strategies.

- Review the homework assignment in class. At the end of class, have students fill in the blanks even if they didn't get the answer themselves. (This increases engagement and encourages self correction.)

- During long holidays, students must still complete one lesson a week. Skill maintenance and development is a year-round task!

- Also, now is the time to get parents involved:

  o Have students ask their parent/guardian to read and sign the Parent Contract on the first page of this book.

  o Throughout the year, students have their parent/guardian review the completed assignments, and initial the bottom of each page.

  o Let parents know that in the beginning of the school year their child will be exposed to unfamiliar material, and it's all right if assignments are not completed. (Here's where the Puzzle Buddy can be a big help!) As the year progresses, more and more of the assignments will be completed. Most important is that their child tries hard, and develops and matures their critical thinking and problem solving strategies. Success is often achieved with steady steps over time.

- On assessment days:

  o Once a month you may conduct an assessment using every fifth lesson. Allow enough time for students to stretch themselves as they work through their challenges.

  o Conduct assessments on a different day than your weekly puzzle time.

  o You may want to snip out the keys on the last "scissor" page. This way your students won't have access to the monthly assessments' answer keys.

  o On the days your students do the assessment lessons (every fifth lesson), you may collect all books and record the results on the Parent Contract page (page one).

  o Review the preceding lessons quickly to assure yourself about the quality of your students' work at home, and return the books the following day.

  o Check for parent/guardian initials on each lesson page, and confirm that there is Puzzle Buddy information on the inside front cover.

- Additional assessment ideas:

  o Daily Puzzle Clues (D.P.C.)
  Give the students 1-2 problems daily from their weekly assigned puzzle. Similar to D.O.L. and excellent for intentional teachable moments.

  o Weekly Puzzle Quiz
  Give your students a 5-10 question quiz from the assigned weekly puzzle. After they finish, have them pass the paper to another student and correct together as a class. You may have the students turn the papers in and monitor their progress.

  o Refer to the Helpful Hints on pages 13-15.

STEP 4: Summer Enrichment Program:

> **GOALS:**
> 1. Students become year-round learners.
> 2. Students maintain learned skills.
> 3. Students are introduced to some new skills required in the next grade.

- If you have sufficient lessons remaining at the end of the school year, these books make an excellent summer transition program. Finally, a summer math program everyone can do!

- Using the book this way helps students maintain the grade level skills they've just acquired, and introduces some of the skills they'll need to be effective, receptive learners in their new grade. Your students will look 'math-smart' with their new teacher!

- Teachers will want to communicate with their students' parents about how important it is that students continue to work and maintain their skills during the summer. The lessons at the end of this book have a blend of the grade skills students have learned, as well as an introduction to the next grade's skills, offering students the chance to excel in the next grade.

- Remind students to turn in their books to their new teacher when school resumes.

- You may use this book as the summer transition program if you have sufficient lessons remaining. In addition, teachers have been so successful using our books for a summer transition program that we are currently developing a Summer Enrichment Program book series. As soon as our Summer Program is ready, you'll be able to order from our on-line store at puzzlewise.com.

Summer Incentives and Contact Ideas:

Students like to be rewarded for doing a great job, so plan something fun for your students so they know this work is important, that you'll be checking their progress, and that there's a nice surprise waiting for them at the end. Some principals and teachers plan a small party for all the students that completed their book by summer's end; other schools call each family twice during the summer to cheer the students on; some schools have a mid-summer Puzzle Festival. This additional effort will result in huge gains in student development, and will also result in a much more effective teaching experience in the Fall when students spend less time re-learning the skills they were supposed to retain!

Helpful Hints to Ensure
Student Success: Teachers

Genre of Crossword Puzzles

As you begin using the crossword puzzles with your students, it's important to help your students understand the genre of crossword puzzles. For example, students may wonder why there is a "1 across" clue and a "3 across" clue – but no "2 across". They also need to learn the strategies of completing a crossword puzzle (e.g. use the answers within other clues to figure out the answer for an unknown clue, and first answer the questions you know and later do the questions you don't know).

The best way to teach your students the genre of crossword puzzles is to follow the "gradual release of responsibility" model (Pearson and Gallagher 1983[1]), explicitly presenting crossword strategies and then gradually handing over responsibility while modeling and guiding.

First, model the strategies used in figuring out a crossword puzzle. Refer to the *Guide for Teachers and Parents* for introducing new concepts. Demonstrate the reading, writing, and mathematical problem solving as you "think aloud". Demonstrate how you use classroom tools (e.g. glossaries, dictionaries, math books, calculators, rulers) and prior knowledge to solve the puzzles. Model what you do when you come across a clue you can't solve. Model many times – one demonstration isn't enough. It's better to have many short demonstrations than one long demonstration. Next, begin solving puzzles in a large group setting (Step 1 of Guide). This is a shared endeavor! Participate with your students in problem solving and completing the puzzle; you lead and support as they do the work. Try to get the children to tell you what to write on the puzzle. Encourage students to share their thinking behind their recommendations.

When students are capable of further responsibility, break the students into small groups and step back from direct participation. Monitor your students and then assess whether you need to do further demonstrations. Pay attention to the challenges they are facing. Use this information to plan further demonstrations, which don't need to be done just by you – recruit some of your students who are excelling at solving crossword puzzles. Be sure the students "think aloud" as they share their answers and strategies.

Finally, when you feel your students have a strong sense of how to solve crosswords, have your students work independently. First, have them work independently in the classroom (Step 2 of Guide), and then, after some repeated successes, have students practice their crossword skills as homework (Step 3 of Guide). Continually assess your students as they work on their crossword skills. Ask questions to learn what strategies and mathematical skills they're using.

Value of Crossword Puzzles

Not only is it important that your students know HOW to figure out crossword puzzles, but it's also important they know WHY someone would want to do them. Neglecting this aspect could result in lower motivation. Here are some ideas to help your students understand the value of crossword puzzles:

- **Challenge your students to see where they can find crossword puzzles**; create a class list and maybe even post examples on a bulletin board. Students are likely to bring in examples from restaurant place mats, cereal boxes, TV guides, newspapers, magazines, etc. As students contribute to the list, ask them to predict the reasons the authors wanted to publish a crossword puzzle.

- **Have your students create a survey to find out some statistics of who completes crossword**

1 *Pearson, P.D. & Gallagher, M.C., (1983). The instruction of reading comprehension. Contemporary Educational Psychology, 8: 317-344.*

PUZZLEWISE™

puzzles, how often, and the origin of the puzzles (e.g. magazines, newspapers, books, etc.). Students can survey family members , faculty members and students in the school as well as community groups such as firefighters, police officers, Rotary Clubs and senior citizen centers. Work this into your math curriculum by having students graph the results of the survey. Do you see a trend with age groups? Gender? Why do they think that's so? Part of the survey should include a section where people share why they like crossword puzzles (if they do). For example, students may learn that people like the intellectual exercise provided by crossword puzzles and that puzzles fill up wasted time when a person is waiting for a bus or a doctor's appointment.

• Cruciverbalist: If you encounter the clue of "a 14 letter word that means crossword puzzle fan," this is the answer. Do some internet research and find out about crossword puzzle tournaments. Ask your students why people participate in these competitions. Maybe your class wants to create a class or school wide crossword puzzle tournament.

• Invite your students' family (including grandparents) to come into the classroom and sit on a "crossword puzzle panel" where students ask them why, when and how they solve crossword puzzles. When you have these people in the room, emphasize how these people rarely complete a crossword puzzle. Make the comparison of a famous sports figure – just as they do not play the game perfectly, it's not expected that the students complete every puzzle perfectly. Make sure the value is placed on the problem solving and sharing of strategies – not on the "right answer."

• Get your students' families to support this work! Share with your students' parents how these particular crossword puzzles have many benefits – such as they help prepare students for state standardized tests. Don't overemphasize the test preparation – be sure you communicate the many other benefits of crosswords as well.

Working Crossword Puzzles into Your Class Schedule

As described in our Guide for Teachers and Parents, after introducing the mathematical crossword puzzles to your class, you may want your students to complete a crossword puzzle each week as homework and then complete one in class per month as an assessment. There are a variety of strategies when using these crossword puzzles in the classroom. Here are some suggestions:

1. Work the puzzles into your daily math time.

2. Have a daily puzzle time (just as many classrooms have a daily silent reading time).

3. Have students work on their puzzles as "bell work" at the beginning of class as a transition to academics.

4. Place the students into puzzle teams where they work together on a regular basis to solve the puzzles.

5. When students complete their math assignments, make this one of their choice assignments. (Consider offering extra credit for puzzle work.)

6. Rather than doing the traditional "daily computation problems" that many classrooms do, assign crossword puzzle clues instead.

Remember, it's critical that students communicate about their problem solving and crossword puzzle strategies. Most state tests require students to share their thinking, so it's important that students get in the habit of doing so – both verbally and in writing. Crossword puzzles can foster communication as students explain and justify their answers to one another.

Be sure you're using the crossword puzzles as a tool to encourage more communication within your classroom. By sharing their thoughts with classmates, students have the opportunity to see the perspectives and methods of others, leading to expanded mental agility and increasingly creative strategizing.

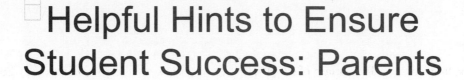

Helpful Hints to Ensure Student Success: Parents

Recommendations for Parents and Guardians

Whether you are a home schooling parent or one who just wants to encourage additional math skill practice, read through the Helpful Hints for classroom teachers. Follow the guidelines where it makes sense to do so. As stated in the teachers' directions, it's critical that students communicate their strategies and problem solving.

If your child doesn't have another child with whom to communicate – then here are some great options:

1. **Communicate** with your child about the strategies and problem solving involved in completing the crosswords.

2. **Partner with other parents and their children**, allowing the children time to share their answers along with their reasoning.

3. **Partner your child with a senior** who enjoys crosswords so they can work them together.

4. **Start a puzzle club**. Have your child send out invitations to join the club that could meet weekly, biweekly or monthly. Include crosswords and other puzzles such as word jumbles and word searches.

Here are some hints to help your child complete the crossword puzzles in this book:

1. **Carry the puzzle book in the car** so it's available during car rides, waiting room visits, and other "I'm bored" times.

2. **Alternate completing answers**. Your child may answer the "across" clues and you may answer the "down" clues. Take turns completing answers.

3. Use the crossword puzzles as a **form of assessment** to help you plan the math instruction for the day. For example, if your child struggles with the puzzle clue, "3 quarters plus 1 nickel = _____ cents," then focus your daily math lesson on similar problems.

4. It's very important to understand that in the beginning of the school year your child is being exposed to unfamiliar material, and it's **all right if your child doesn't finish all the problems**.

As long as your child makes a good attempt to finish the assignment every week, that's sufficient. As the year advances, and more skills are learned and matured, more of each puzzle will be completed. It's more important that your child tries hard, because success is often achieved with steady steps over time.

5. Remember, if you want your child to embrace crossword puzzles as a leisure time activity, you need to model working on crossword puzzles **during your "off time,"** too! When you show yourself as a life long learner who enjoys puzzles, your child is likely to do the same.

6. Make sure there's **laughter** worked into your puzzle time, so crosswords are not "a chore." Do all you can to make the puzzles enjoyable, appealing and worthwhile to your child!

PUZZLEWISE™

The PuzzleWise™ Foundation

Like you, we believe in service to others. There are great needs of all kinds in our families, our communities, and our world. We want to be part of the solution, and we've established a non-profit foundation to address some of these needs both locally and globally. A portion of sales will be given to the foundation for the growth and well-being of those in need.

Our goal is to establish a network of organic food restaurants in communities across America where families and people can receive a healthy, tasty dinner at cost. Too often our friends and neighbors come home after a hard day's work, and there's no time to prepare a healthy meal for themselves and their children. We rely too much on processed foods loaded with impurities, and the foods we eat further compound the personal and social problems we face today.

Instead, families and individuals can have a balanced dinner rich in vitamins and minerals, which tastes great and empowers their bodies, and only pay the actual cost. We further envision these restaurants becoming a place where families gather not only for food, but also for social connection and for rebuilding the relationships of a healthy community.

We aim to establish a model that serves 100% of the families in our communities. The restaurants will become community focal points promoting a common goal of finding ways to help its members: mowing lawns for the eldery, helping families move furniture or start up a business, organizing youth to maintain parks, helping to establish shelters, seeking care for someone with medical or dental needs, working on someone's car, finding a job for someone in need… There are many ways to rebuild our communities, and many people willing to help if they only knew how!

Yes, this is an ambitious program, and we'll do what we can. To accomplish the possible, we all have to work together and put forward our best attitudes to match our strongest attributes. And we can't do it alone; we have to do it together, as a **TEAM**: **T**ogether **E**verybody **A**chieves **M**ore.

"Anyone can count the seeds in an apple. No one can count the apples in a seed." (Anonymous)

We hope you'll like our books and support our common cause. Thank you!

With our best wishes,

Matt and Daniel

Graph Your Progress

Record your personal goal for each puzzle, then shade in each line of the graph to show the number correct.

Lesson	Goal	5	10	15	20	25
1	___/25					
2	___/25					
3	___/25					
4	___/25					
5	___/25					
6	___/25					
7	___/25					
8	___/25					
9	___/25					
10	___/25					30
11	___/30					
12	___/30					
13	___/30					
14	___/30					
15	___/30					
16	___/30					
17	___/30					
18	___/30					
19	___/30					
20	___/30					35
21	___/35					
22	___/35					
23	___/35					
24	___/35					
25	___/35					
26	___/35					
27	___/35					
28	___/35					
29	___/35					
30	___/35					40
31	___/40					
32	___/40					
33	___/40					
34	___/40					
35	___/40					
36	___/40					
37	___/40					
38	___/40					
39	___/40					
40	___/40					
41	___/45					
42	___/45					
43	___/45					
44	___/45					
45	___/45					

ACROSS

3 $0.778 + 0.778 + 0.778 = N \times 0.778$
5 The number of legs on a spider.
7 3D shape with six congruent sides.
9 There are 206 of these in the adult body.
12 Pattern 5, 10, 9, 14, 13, 18, N.
14 $20 \div N = 4$
16 What is the 10th number in this list? 5, 9, 13, 17, …
19 Chance of rolling an odd number on a six-sided die = N/6.
20 The difference between 10 and Y, when Y = 8.
21 An average cat weighs about 9.5 pounds. 7 cats weigh about 70 pounds. Right or wrong?
23 Cycle next to a friend and stay the distance apart. Your paths are ____ .
24 16 steps up to the balcony. Climb halfway up and 7 steps more. How many steps left to the top?

DOWN

1 Eighty legs. How many spiders?
2 Jack measures the floor in square feet. Koko measures the same floor in square meters. Who has the greatest number?
3 $36 \div 3$
4 A ____ diagram has loops to show how things are related.
6 Approximate number of hundreds in $440 - 435 + 201$.
8 A baker's dozen.
10 $9 \times N = 63$
11 The number of endpoints of a line.
13 Number of tenths in 0.8.
15 Number of dozens needed to make 4 dozen into 6 dozen.
17 Remainder when $80 \div 7$.
18 Number of lines of symmetry in an equilateral triangle.
22 $2 \times 2 \times 2 \times N = $ sixteen.

1. A fraction of this group of circles is shaded.

Which of the following groups is shaded to show the fraction with the same value?

○ A

○ B

○ C

○ D

2. Trevor wants to build a fenced area in his backyard for his rabbit. For which of the following would he need to know the perimeter of the area?

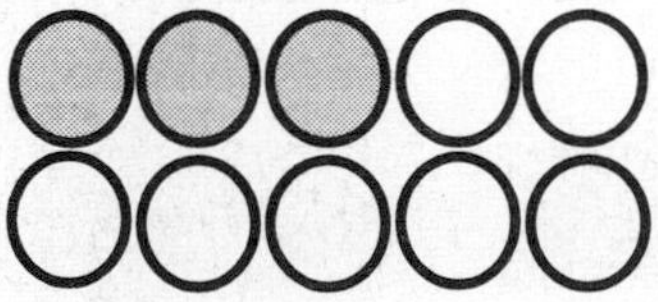

○ A   Determining how much grass will be enclosed

○ B   Determining how much water his rabbit will need

○ C   Determining the diameter of the food dish

○ D   Determining how many feet of fencing are needed to go around the area

3. Look at the number pattern below:

$$128, 64, 32, 16, \ldots$$

What are the next two numbers in the number pattern? Write your answer on the lines below.

The next two numbers are: _____, _____

Explain the rule you used to find the next two numbers in the pattern in the space provided below.

| |
| |
| |
| |
| |
| |
| |

"Do not be timid about your actions. All life is an experiment." — Ralph Waldo Emerson, Philosopher

ACROSS

2 How many kids in a set of quadruplets?

4 The letter H has this many lines of symmetry.

5 One-third of twice C, when C = 3.

7 Pattern Machine: Input = 10, 14, 20, 26. Output = 5, N, 10, 13.

9 A number > 1 whose only divisors are 1 and itself.

11 Recipe uses 2 eggs to make 4 servings. If 12 servings, how many eggs?

14 Number of musicians in a quartet.

15 If two things have the same chance of happening, they are ___ . (Two words.)

17 Compare: 1/2 of a bunch of 6 bananas (more less same) 1/4 of a dozen bananas.

19 Eli estimates 45.5 × 5 is about 250. Is he right or wrong?

20 243, 81, 27, 9, N, 1.

22 0.98 = 9 tenths + ___ hundredths.

23 Hot air balloon can lift 1000 pounds. Each bear weighs 150 pounds. Max # bears on balloon?

24 Triskaidecaphobia is the fear of this number.

DOWN

1 2/7 of my shirts are pink. 14 shirts, how many are not pink?

2 If your street is 4000 meters long, how many kilometers long is your street?

3 Triangle with two equal sides.

6 $10.00 is how many dimes?

8 The first prime after 20.

10 6/5 (more less same) 1/2 .

12 Railroad tracks are examples of ___ lines.

13 2/5 of $20 is how many dollars?

16 Bart bought two $6 harmonicas and four $1.50 nose flutes. Total dollars?

18 Compare: 19/20 (more less same) 20/21.

21 1 + (2 ÷ 3) + 4 = (1 + 2) + (3 + 4). Is that right or wrong?

1. Which of the following have at least two sides that appear to be parallel?

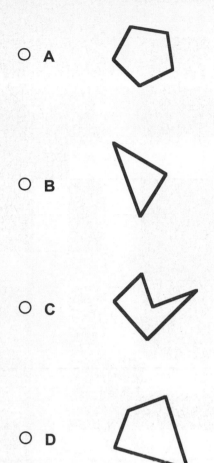

○ A

○ B

○ C

○ D

2. Abby wants to increase her running speed. What conclusions can be made from the information on the graph above?

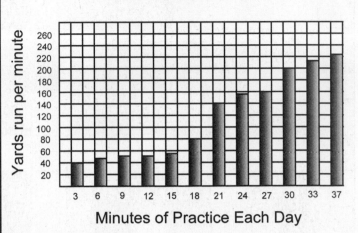

Speed People Run

○ A The number of yards run per minute goes down with practice.

○ B More than 18 minutes practice doesn't increase running rate.

○ C Practicing 12 minutes a day is better than practicing 9 minutes per day.

○ D Overall, the speed of running increases as the number of practice minutes increases.

3. Ginny has a collection of 48 stuffed animals. She plans to give all of her stuffed animals to her six friends, giving each of them an equal number of stuffed animals. In the space provided below, write a number sentence that can be used to find how many stuffed animals each friend will receive.

ACROSS

1 Length = 8 inches × B. Inches when B = 3?
5 Same number of nickels and dimes. $3.00, how many coins?
10 0.5 units to the right of 7.5 on a number line.
12 7000 grains per pound. Grains in 22 quivers = N × 7000.
13 One step forwards, two steps back. Do this ten times; how many steps back are you?
15 Which has exactly two factors: 8, 13, 15, 21?
16 The mean of 2 and 10.
17 $3/2 - 1/2 = N$
18 A whole number and a fraction together make a ____ number.
19 Mode of 7, 3, 3, 3, 7, 7, 8, 9, 7.
21 To the nearest 100, approximate 49.47 × 12.
22 1/1000 of a meter.
23 1/2 of 396 = ____ + 137.

DOWN

1 7 × 72 = (7 × 70) + 7 × N
2 1 & 1/3 = N/3
3 Number of horns on a triceratops.
4 1 is a prime number. Right or wrong?
6 Outline of door is this shape.
7 Perimeter of square = 32. Side of square = N.
8 Letter chosen at random. Probability vowel (more less same) probability consonant.
9 10, ____ , 18, 22, 26.
11 A 16 gallon gas tank is 3/4 full. Gallons remaining?
14 I am a multiple of 6 and 9. I am less than 20.
15 Number of lines of symmetry in the numeral 8.
20 630 ÷ 70

1. Monica has two spinners.

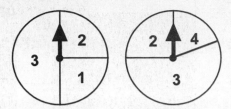

She spins each arrow once and writes down the sum of the two numbers. How many different sums are possible?

- ○ **A** 4
- ○ **B** 6
- ○ **C** 5
- ○ **D** 9

2. Look at the shaded figure below.

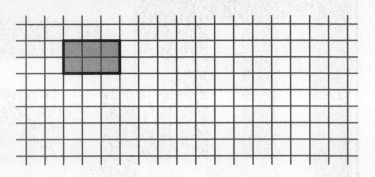

If the length and width of the figure were tripled, what would be the area of the figure?

- ○ **A** 6 square units
- ○ **B** 12 square units
- ○ **C** 24 square units
- ○ **D** 54 square units

3. The students at Riverside School won a reading contest with a prize of milkshakes for every student who participated. The chart below shows the types of milkshakes available and the number of student who requested each type.

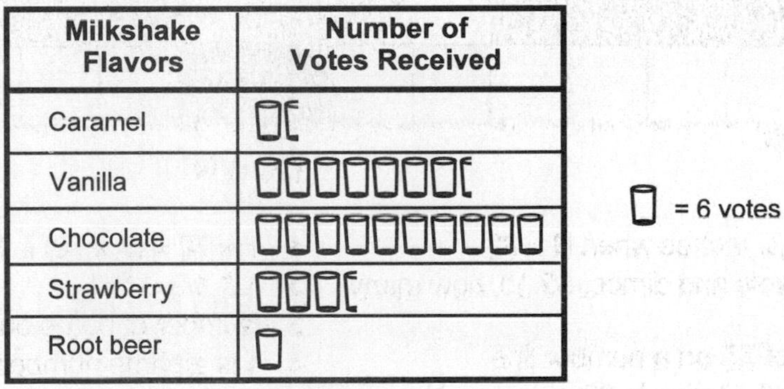

Milkshake Flavors	Number of Votes Received
Caramel	▯▮
Vanilla	▯▯▯▯▯▯▮
Chocolate	▯▯▯▯▯▯▯▯▯▯
Strawberry	▯▯▯▮
Root beer	▯

▯ = 6 votes

How many more students requested vanilla than strawberry?
Explain your answer using words, numbers, or pictures.

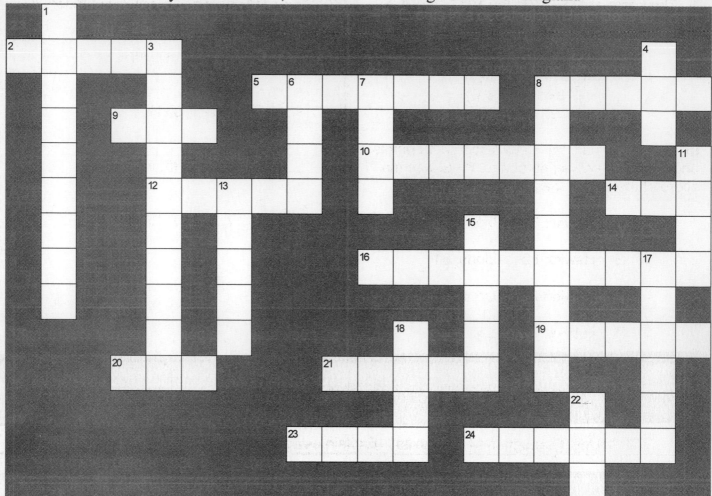

ACROSS

2 2 is a factor of 12. Right or wrong?

5 Triangle with no equal sides.

8 $36 = 2 \times 2 \times 3 \times N$

9 N, 5, 10, 9, 18, 17, 34, 33, 66.

10 Number of thousandths in 0.016

12 1/10 = N thirtieths.

14 Missing digit: $35 \times 35 = 12$ ___5

16 Which has more than two factors: 31, 39, 41, 43?

19 Right or wrong? It is impossible to walk 10 miles in one day.

20 90 minutes before 11:30 = ___ o'clock.

21 A square is translated so that all the points go up 3 and right 2. If one corner started at (4,4), that corner would end at (7,6). Right or wrong?

23 $100 \div []$, if $[] = 25$.

24 A right angle is N°.

DOWN

1 Type of graph using line segments.

3 The product of 5 and 7.

4 30 feet = N yards.

6 A 3D shape with a circular base and a vertex.

7 Compare: 5/16 (more less same) 1/2.

8 Perimeter of a 5 × 6 rectangle.

11 Length of snake > 9 feet. Snake (more less same) 9 feet.

13 Dividing by zero is faulty. Right or wrong?

15 100 ÷ 9.2 is about 20. Right or wrong?

17 An obtuse angle measures > N°.

18 Approximate number of hundreds in 299 + 50 + 50.

22 Events in a decathalon (Hint: "deca").

1. The score at the end of the first half of the Hawks-Lions game is shown here.

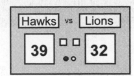

In the second half, the Hawks scored 43 points and the Lions scored 49 points. What was the score at the end of the game?

- ○ **A**   Hawks: 81   Lions: 80
- ○ **B**   Hawks: 82   Lions: 81
- ○ **C**   Hawks: 75   Lions: 86
- ○ **D**   Hawks: 75   Lions: 77

2. Which list contains only prime numbers?

- ○ **A**   3, 7, 11, 17, 19
- ○ **B**   1, 3, 5, 9, 19
- ○ **C**   1, 6, 8, 15, 17
- ○ **D**   7, 11, 13, 15, 19

3. (a) Ben needs to bake enough cookies to fill 20 boxes with 5 cookies in each box. Ben plans on baking 3 batches with 18 cookies in each batch.

Will he make enough to fill the boxes? Explain using words, numbers, or pictures.

(b) Write a number sentence to show how many batches of cookies, with 18 in each batch, Ben will need to make to fill his boxes.

ACROSS

2 7 is a factor of 35. Right or wrong?

3 1 third = N sixths.

5 Find the composite: 23, 29, 49, 61.

6 Rule: Multiply by 1.5 and round down. Pattern: 4, 6, 9, N, 19, 28.

9 Pattern Machine. Input: 3, 9, 15, 20. Output: 5, 11, 17, N.

10 The closest integer to the left of 11.7 on the number line.

12 A spinner is split into 10 equal regions numbered 1-10. Chance of spinning odd number = 1/N.

14 N/3 = 5 & 1/3.

16 Start with 13. Do this twice: -10, + 5, +2.

17 5 sixths = N sixtieths.

19 8 cats weigh 50 pounds. 16 cats weigh N pounds.

20 Square: 9 area, perimeter ____ .

21 39 ÷ N = 3

DOWN

1 10/16 + 5/16 = N/16

2 A square is a parallelogram. Right or wrong?

4 A diet calls for 1000 mg of vitamin X. How many grams is that?

6 0.678 + 1.989 – 0.5 is approximately what integer?

7 The mean of 10, 20, 30 and 40.

8 Metric measure of length, about the width of your finger.

9 Number of 45° angles in a right angle.

11 Stop sign shape.

13 Area of rectangle = 60 sq. cm. L = 12 cm, W = ____ cm.

14 Compare: Area of triangle with B = 5 and H = 10 (more less same) area of triangle with B = 10 and H = 5.

15 The measure that tells how long something is.

18 The mean of 0 and 6.

1. What is the area of this figure?

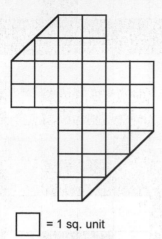

☐ = 1 sq. unit

   ○ **A** 27.5 square units

   ○ **B** 30 square units

   ○ **C** 29.5 square units

   ○ **D** 48 square units

2. Michael used the equation $y = x \times 2$ to fill in the table below.

x	y
3	6
4	8
5	10
9	—

What number completes the table?

   ○ **A** 12   ○ **B** 15

   ○ **C** 18   ○ **D** 27

3. Ariel made brownies for her friends. She wants to pack the brownies in boxes. She packed each box:

   4 brownies long
   2 brownies wide
   3 brownies high

How many brownies does each box hold? Show your work in the space provided below.

Number of Brownies in One Box = _____

"Problems are only opportunities in work clothes." — Henry Kaiser, Builder

ACROSS

2 Abbreviation for "morning".

3 Greatest common factor of 12 and 15.

6 $15 \div @$, if $@ = 1 + 2$.

7 20 is divisible by 2. Right or wrong?

8 Missing digit: $594.792 \div 13.2 = 45.\_\_\_6$

13 M = 9. Compare: 81 / M (more less same) 9.

14 A right triangle's short leg is 1, and its long leg is 6. What's the area?

15 3 flavors ice cream, 3 flavors of toppings. Choose one each, how many possible desserts?

16 8 quarts = ____ gallons.

19 A regular quadrilateral.

21 The average angle measure of a trapezoid.

22 A tessellation is also called this.

23 You can use a compass to draw this.

DOWN

1 Compare: Mean of 4, 5 and 6 (more less same) mean of 3, 6 and 6.

3 $12 = 2 \times 2 \times N$

4 A pair of numbers which tell a location on a map.

5 Pattern: 8, 40, 20, 100, N, 250, 125.

8 Four lines are parallel. They intersect a total of N times.

9 $\$0.35 = N/20$ dollar.

10 $0.3 = N$ hundredths.

11 (4,7) is translated 3 to the right. New position is (7,N).

12 Compare: 8 + 1.05 (more less same) 10.

17 The area of an equilateral triangle with one side = 8 is 24. Right or wrong?

18 5/6 (more less same) 2/3.

20 Which is lesser: acute or obtuse?

1. Which would result in the greatest number?

   ○ **A**   10 squared + 30 squared

   ○ **B**   10 cubed

   ○ **C**   40 squared

   ○ **D** $10 \times 11 \times 12 \times 13$

2. Which of the following is a scalene triangle?

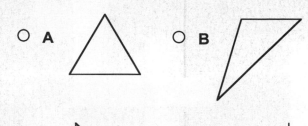

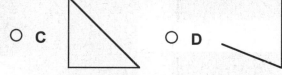

3. Bryan went to the store. He bought a gallon of milk for $3.15, a bag of tortillas for $2.27, and two bags of cookies for $2.59 each. If Bryan pays with a $20 bill, how much change will he receive?

Show your work in the space provided below.

Lesson 7:
"There's a better way to do it. Find it!" — Thomas Edison, Inventor

/25

ACROSS

1 Five 20s in 100. How many in 500?

4 100 pancakes served 34 people. Next week 17 people, about how many pancakes?

5 Perimeter of a 3 × 5 rectangle.

6 If 6 is 1 inch from 0 on a number line, what number is 1 inch to the right of 6?

10 The mean of 20 and 40.

14 Number of lines of symmetry in a square.

15 51 is prime. Right or wrong?

16 A fraction that relates rates.

17 Start with 5. Do this twice: × 3, − 5.

18 Pythagorean Theorem is named for him.

20 $56 \div N = 8$

21 A recipe calls for 1/2 L of milk. How many milliliters of milk is that?

DOWN

2 50% of 20.

3 1000 cubic centimeters.

5 2/3 of a right angle is N°.

7 $88.3 \div 83.8 = 83.8 \div 88.3$. Right or wrong?

8 $165 - 200 + 35$

9 Rule: Divide by 3 and add 3. Pattern: 261, 90, 33, N.

11 This angle is greater than an acute angle but less than an obtuse.

12 $8/100 + 82/100 = N/100$

13 Pattern: abbcd, bccde, cddef, ____ .

14 Area of square = 25. Side of square = N.

15 Right or wrong? It is impossible to eat 10 lemons in one day.

17 Wheels on three unicycles.

19 $20/6 = 3 \& N/6$

1. Which of the following describes a figure that has an area of 32 square centimeters?

○ **A** A rectangle with a length of 8 centimeters and a width of 4 centimeters

○ **B** A rectangle with a length of 9 centimeters and a width of 3 centimeters

○ **C** A square with a length of 6 centimeters and a width of 6 centimeters

○ **D** A triangle that has two sides 10 centimeters long and one side 23 centimeters long

2. The school district is tracking the high and low scores of each game for each of their high school basketball teams.

High School Basketball Scores		
School	Low Scores	High Scores
Central High	42	72
Bayside High	38	63
East Side High	55	71
Jefferson High	43	69
Everett High	45	64

According to the chart above, what is the median low score for the teams?

○ **A** 42   ○ **B** 71

○ **C** 63   ○ **D** 43

3. The rectangle below has an area of 16 square units and a perimeter of 16 units.

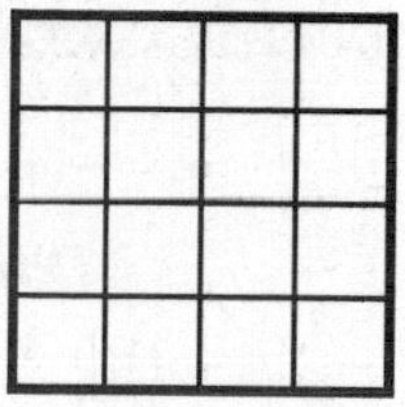

On the grid below, draw a rectangle that has the same area, but a different perimeter, from the rectangle above.

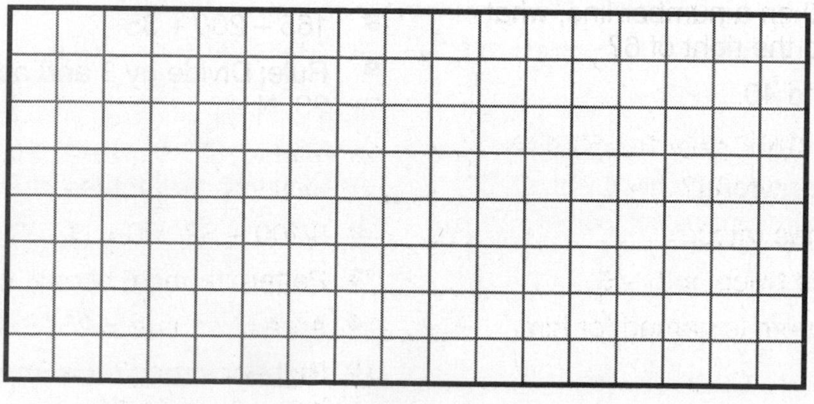

What is the perimeter, in units, of the new rectangle? _____

31

ACROSS

1 $1062 - 963$

4 Nickels in 25 dimes.

6 2 is a factor of 48. Right or wrong?

9 Pattern: 12, 14, 11, 13, 10, 12, 9, N.

11 A triangle can have a 170° angle. Right or wrong?

13 $0.076 = 7$ hundredths + N thousandths.

14 Number of children in one group of quintuplets.

15 Quadrilateral with four right angles.

19 (1,1) is translated 2 right and 3 up. New point: (3,N).

20 A triangle that has all sides the same length can have angles with different degrees. Right or wrong?

22 A number with more than one pair of factors.

23 $\$0.25 = \$N/4$

DOWN

2 Number of equal sides in an equilateral triangle.

3 Same size and shape.

4 Number of 2 digit numbers > or = 50.

5 Prime factorization of 12 is $2 \times N \times 3$.

7 @ = 15, ★ = 5. What is @ ÷ ★?

8 Number of centimeters in a meter.

10 Compare: $65.2 \div 65.5$ (more less same) $65.5 \div 65.2$

12 Number of musicians in a quintet.

15 It is impossible to stay awake for a month. Right or wrong?

16 Compare: 98/99 (more less same) 1.

17 Compare: $8 - 1.5$ (more less same) 6.

18 The area of a rectangle is 20, and the length is 4. The width of the rectangle is 6. Right or wrong?

21 Time for trip < 2 hours. 2 hours (more less same) time for trip.

1. Which group shows the prime factorization of the number 108?

   ○ **A** $2 \times 2 \times 3 \times 3 \times 3$

   ○ **B** 4×27

   ○ **C** $2 \times 2 \times 2 \times 100$

   ○ **D** $25 + 25 + 25 + 25 + 8$

2. The perimeter of the rectangle shown below is 56 centimeters.

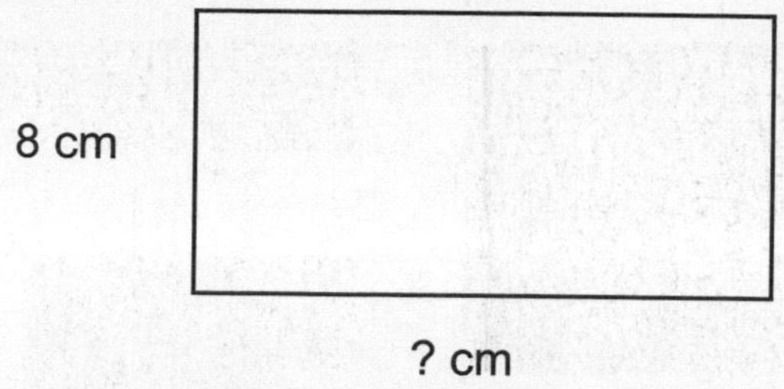

8 cm

? cm

What is the missing measurement of the rectangle?

   ○ **A** 16 cm   ○ **B** 40 cm

   ○ **C** 10 cm   ○ **D** 20 cm

3. John earns money by doing chores for his neighbors. He is paid $8 for raking a lawn, $11 for mowing a lawn, and $4 for weeding a patch of garden.

Last week he mowed two lawns and weeded three patches of garden, then he went to the hardware store and bought a new rake for $14 and new gloves for $7. 25.

How much money did John have left? Show your work in the space provided below.

"One of the secrets of life is to make stepping stones out of stumbling blocks." — Jack Penn, Author

ACROSS

1 The mean of 5 and 15.
2 9/5 = N & 4/5
4 12 sixths = N halves.
7 1 × 1 (more less same) 1 ÷ 1
10 Box of 12 costs $3.60. Unit price = N¢
12 1000 of these make a kilometer.
13 Pascal was from this country.
14 Square: area 1, perimeter ____ .
15 1 inch = 2 units on a number line. 3 inches to the right of 5 = N.
16 From (0,0) go 4 right, 4 up, 4 right, 4 down. How far from (0,0) are you?
17 11/6 + 1/6 = N sixths
20 Rule: Add 3 and divide by 2. Pattern: 11, 7, 5, N.
21 Find the composite: 89, 53, 46, 73.
22 Secret Rule: {1, 6, 4, 10} matches {N, 11, 9, 15}.
23 A fraction whose numerator is greater than or equal to its denominator is an ____ fraction.

DOWN

1 3/2 + 1/2 = N
3 1 tsp = 3 grams. Grams in 3 tsp?
4 11.004 + 2.105 + 1.955 is approximately what integer?
5 U.S. temperature is measured in these kind of degrees.
6 99 × 101 × 1 × 1 (more less same) 101 × 99
8 Start with 5. Do this twice: + 1, × 2.
9 Quadrilateral with one pair of parallel sides.
11 Perimeter of rectangle = 30 sq. cm. L = 12 cm, W = ____ cm.
18 An equilateral triangle can have a right angle. Right or wrong?
19 A regular octagon has ____ pairs of parallel sides.

1. Each letter in the word

MISSISSIPPI

is written on a separate piece of paper and put into a bag. One of the pieces of paper is selected from the bag at random. What is the probability that the piece of paper selected will be the letter **_S_**?

○ **A**   2 / 11   ○ **B**   4 / 11

○ **C**   1 / 4   ○ **D**   4 / 9

2. On Tuesday, a train left Washington DC at 7:15 A.M. and arrived in New York City at 2:46 P.M. If there were no stops, how long did the trip take?

○ **A**   19 hours, 31 minutes

○ **B**   7 hours, 33 minutes

○ **C**   7 hours, 31 minutes

○ **D**   5 hours, 33 minutes

3. This table shows the number of veggie burgers sold at Steadman's Burger Palace on Monday.

Veggie Burgers	Number Sold
Single	32
Double	21
Triple	13
Special	16
Kid's Meal	17

Each Single and each Kid's Meal uses 1 patty. Doubles use 2 patties. Triples and Specials each use 3 patties.

How many total hamburger patties were used at Steadman's Burger Palace yesterday?

Explain your work using words, numbers, or pictures.

ACROSS

1 0.080 = N/1000

3 $0.10 = 1/N dollar.

6 The angle sum of a pentagon, in degrees, is 500 + N.

9 The number of square units which cover a region.

10 2 is a factor of 17. Right or wrong?

11 5/3 + 10/3

12 Which is greater: acute or obtuse?

14 4000 lbs = N tons.

15 56 = 2 × 2 × 2 × N

18 A triangle that has all angles the same size must have all sides the same length. Right or wrong?

20 Compare: 20 − 1.2 (more less same) 19.

22 A tiling of shapes that fit together with no gaps.

23 Roman numeral 1009 spells this word.

DOWN

2 How many units apart are (33,3) and (3,3)?

3 A type of quadrilateral with one pair of parallel sides.

4 3D shape, looks like a round can.

5 The area of a 5 by 6 rectangle is 30. Right or wrong?

7 A football referee holds his arms up in the air in a ____ position to show that a field goal has been scored.

8 B = 20. Compare: B − 10 (more less same) 9.

11 Pattern 100, 50, 52, 26, 28, N, 16.

13 If & = 4, what is 40 ÷ & ?

16 2 × 40 = 80, so 0.2 × 40 = N

17 (4,2) is translated 1 right and 3 up. New point: (5,N)

19 3 different shirts, 3 different pants. Number of outfits?

21 Least common multiple of 6 and 3.

1. Brianna bought 7 stickers priced at $0.30 each. She used a coupon for $0.75 off the total cost. Which number sentence can be used to find how much money Brianna needed in order to buy the stickers?

○ **A** $(7 \times 0.30) - 0.75 = 1.35$

○ **B** $(7 + 0.30) + 0.75 = 8.05$

○ **C** $(7 - 0.30) + 0.75 = 7.45$

○ **D** $(7 \times 0.75) - 0.30 = 4.95$

2. Look at the grid below.

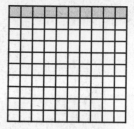

What part of this grid is shaded?

○ **A** $\dfrac{10}{50}$ ○ **B** 10

○ **C** $\dfrac{10}{100}$ ○ **D** $\dfrac{50}{100}$

3. Look at the number pattern below.

72, 63, 64, 55, 56, 47, 48, _____, _____

What are the next two numbers in the number pattern? Explain your work using words, numbers, or pictures.

"Light tomorrow with today!" — Elizabeth Barrett Browning, Author

/30

ACROSS

3 8 cats weigh 40 pounds. 16 cats weigh N pounds.

7 Compare: A number plotted to the left of three on a number line (more less same) three.

8 The mean of 0 and 10.

10 A "turn" is also called a ___ .

12 Find the composite: 2, 23, 37, 42.

14 M = 25. Compare: M / 5 (more less same) 6.

18 36 ÷ N = 6

20 2 sevenths = N seventieths.

23 Fractions which have the same value are ___ .

24 Pattern Machine. Input: 3, 9, 15, 20. Output: 6, 12, 18, N.

26 A spinner is split into 10 equal regions numbered 1-10. Chance of spinning even number = 1/N.

27 A regular pentagon has ___ pairs of parallel sides.

28 45 × 0.2

DOWN

1 Compare: Area of 6 by 5 rectangle (more less same) area of triangle with base 6 and height 12.

2 N/3 = 2 & 1/3

4 9/16 + 6/16 = N/16

5 Measurement system used by most countries in the world.

6 If two lines cross at a right angle, the lines are ___ .

8 Greatest common factor of 12 and 16.

9 Square: side 1, perimeter ___ .

11 7 is a factor of 21. Right or wrong?

13 Archimedes yelled this as he leapt from the bath.

15 Rule: Multiply by 1.5 and round down. Pattern: 2, 3, 4, N.

16 1/6 of a right angle is N°.

17 2000 centimeters is longer than 4 meters. Right or wrong?

19 Perimeter of 1 × 3 rectangle.

21 4 quarts.

22 1 third = N ninths.

24 0.52 + 1.99 − 0.45 is approximately what integer?

25 Start with 30. Do this twice: − 17, + 5, + 2.

1. Marty's class made a pie chart of how they spent their class time for one week.

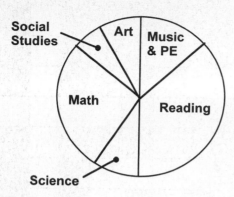

Approximately how much of Marty's class time was spent on Art?

    A 1/12   B 1/8

    C 1/6   D 1/4

2. All the students in Mr. Freeman's class brought cookies to school in the lunches on Friday. Jose brought only a sandwich. Based on this information, which **must be true**?

    A If Jose brought only a sandwich, then he was not in school on Monday.

    B If Jose brought only a sandwich, then he is in Ms. Ohlsen's class.

    C If Jose brought only a sandwich, then he is in Mr. Freeman's class.

    D If Jose brought only a sandwich, then he is not in Mr. Freeman's class.

3. The perimeter of triangle *ABC* below is 32 meters. What is the length of side *AC*?

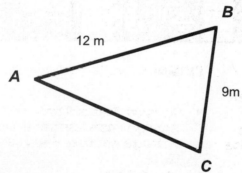

Explain your answer using words, pictures, or numbers.

"The things that count most in life are usually the things that cannot be counted." — Bernard Meltzer, Attorney

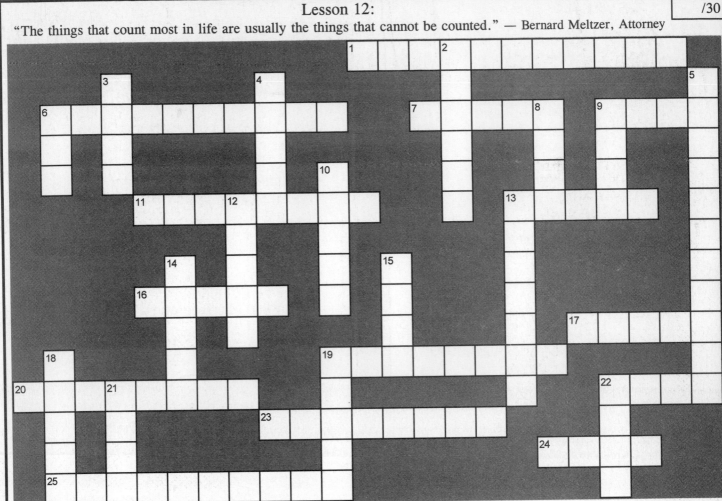

ACROSS

1 1/2 of a liter is N milliliters.

6 100 pancakes served 28 people. Next week 7 people, about how many pancakes?

7 N/10 dollar = 70 cents.

9 18/3 (more less same) 5.

11 Start with 2. Do this twice: × 3, − 1.

13 Missing digit: 4467.9855 ÷ 56.65 = 78.8___

16 1 kg is heavier than 1 lb. Right or wrong?

17 The area of a 7 by 8 rectangle is 56. Right or wrong?

19 The twenty yard line and the thirty yard line are ___ lines on a football field.

20 The longest measure across a circle.

22 Number of right angles needed to make 360°.

23 A line segment connecting vertices of a polygon (not an edge).

24 N, 8, 7, 14, 13, 26, 25, 50, 49.

25 75 ÷ [], if [] = 3.

DOWN

2 Number of sides on the polygon around the border of a Susan B. Anthony dollar.

3 Compare: Mean of 0, 5, 10, 5 (more less same) mean of 8, 8, 4, and 1.

4 2 is a factor of 18. Right or wrong?

5 Tells the size of the parts of a fraction.

6 $16 = 2 \times 2 \times 2 \times N$

8 How many possible dinners if you choose 1 each of 3 entrees, 3 vegetables?

9 Compare: A number plotted to the right of three on a number line (more less same) three.

10 Greatest common factor of 28 and 35.

12 Which is lesser: right or obtuse?

13 9.2 + 6.8

14 0.4 × 20

15 Number of thousandths in 0.004.

18 The area of a right triangle with legs 8 and 2.

19 A flat surface is a model of this.

21 R = 11. Compare: 10 + R (more less same) 20.

22 (7,3) is translated 1 right and 1 up. New point: (8,N).

1. There are three red, two yellow, and two green gumballs in a bag. Without looking in the bag, what are the chances of picking a green gumball out of the bag?

- ○ **A**   One out of seven chances
- ○ **B**   Two out of seven chances
- ○ **C**   Three out of seven chances
- ○ **D**   Two out of three chances

2. Maggie made 4 times as many goals during soccer season as her brother Peter. If K represents the number of goals scored by Maggie, which expression can be used to find the number of goals Peter scored this season?

- ○ **A** $K + 4$
- ○ **B** $K \div 4$
- ○ **C** $K - 4$
- ○ **D** $K \times 4$

3. Look at the number sentence below.

$$682 = 15 \text{ tens} + \triangle \text{ hundreds} + \square \text{ ones.}$$

Find one number for $\triangle$ and one number for $\square$ that make the number sentence true. Show your work in the space provided below.

$\triangle$ = _____ $\square$ = _____

"The times change and we change with them." — John Owen, Poet

ACROSS

1 Number of mL in 6 L.

4 (7,3) is translated 1 right and 1 up. New point: (N,4).

8 Way to show data which resembles a tree is a ___ plot. (Three words.)

10 $36 = 2 \times N \times 3 \times 3$

11 Perimeter of 6 × 10 rectangle.

15 Heads comes up on a coin flip about N times out of 30.

16 How many gallon jugs will 12 quarts fill?

17 The mean of 6 and 10.

18 Mathematician who said "I think, therefore I am."

20 Square: perimeter 4, side ___ .

21 0.017 = 1 hundredth + N thousandths.

23 A regular hexagon has ___ lines of symmetry.

24 Two acute angles added together can form a right angle. Right or wrong?

25 One step forwards, two steps back. Do this 15 times, how many steps back are you?

27 $6/2 - 4/2 = N/2$

28 $3 \& 3/5 = N/5$

29 $49 \div N = 7$

DOWN

2 Compare: Area of 3 by 4 rectangle (more less same) area of triangle with base 12 and height 2.

3 One cubic centimeter.

5 Rule: Double and add 3. Pattern: 3, 9, 21, N.

6 2 fifths = N tenths.

7 5/2 is plotted to the left of # on number line. Compare: # (more less same) 5/2.

9 $30/90 = N/45$

12 Secret Rule: {1, 2, 3, 4} matches {4, 8, N, 16}.

13 The order in which you do calculations is the order of ___ .

14 3 is a factor of 9. Right or wrong?

19 Find the prime: 55, 11, 12, 21.

22 2.52 + 10.50 + 0.01 is approximately 13. Right or wrong?

26 I am a multiple of 5 and 10. I am less than 20.

27 @ = 20, ★ = 2. What is @ ÷ ★ ?

1. Rewrite this expression:

$4^3 =$

  ○ **A** 4 + 4 + 4

  ○ **B** 4 × 4 × 4

  ○ **C** 3 + 3 + 3 + 3

  ○ **D** 3 × 3 × 3 × 3

2. Mrs. Chen is 42 years old. Her daughter is 9 years old. The age of Mrs. Chen, her husband, and their daughter adds up to 83. Which equation can be used to determine the age of Mrs. Chen's husband?

  ○ **A** 83 + 42 + 9 = a

  ○ **B** 42 + a = 83 + 9

  ○ **C** 42 + 9 = 83 + a

  ○ **D** 42 + 9 + a = 83

3. Central School held book reading contest. On Monday, the principal made this chart of the results by grade level.

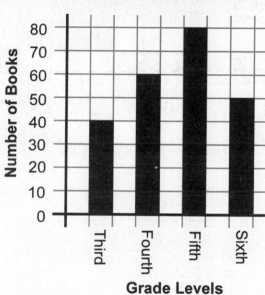

Number of Books Read by Grade at Central School

On Tuesday, an additional 25 books were recorded by teachers in fourth grade, 12 by third grade teachers, and 16 by sixth grade teachers. How many books, total, were read by the students at Central School? Explain your answer using words, pictures, or numbers.

/30

"Let no one ever come to you without leaving better and happier." — Mother Theresa, Missionary

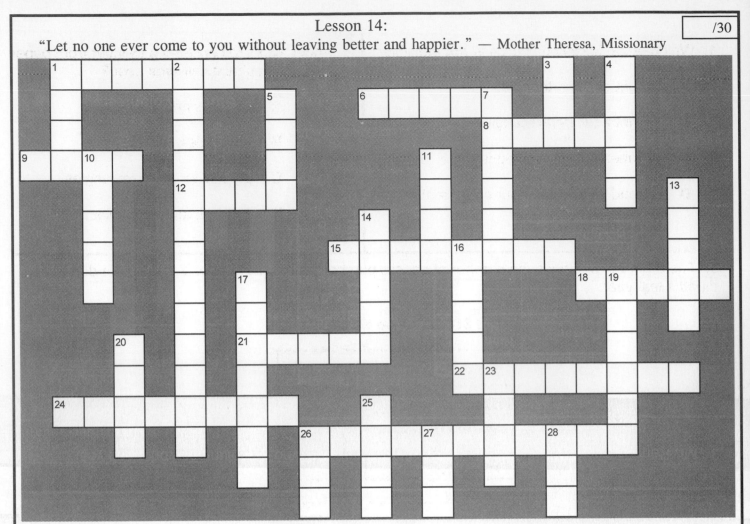

ACROSS

1 Greatest common factor of 15 and 30.

6 Number of 45° angles needed to make 360°.

8 27 is divisible by 2. Right or wrong?

9 2/3 (more less same) 3/2.

12 F = 9. Compare: 3 × F (more less same) 32.

15 Pattern 10, 13, 12, 15, 14, 17, 16, N.

18 The area of a 1 by 2 rectangle is 3. Right or wrong?

21 11/2 dollars = 5 dollars and N cents.

22 A line segment has two; a ray has one.

24 The border between Oregon and California and the border between Oregon and Washington are roughly ___ lines.

26 Value of "5" in 1.045 = 5 ___ .

DOWN

1 Missing digit: $32.55 ÷ 3.1 = $10.___0

2 When two events can occur with the same probability, they are ___ . (Two words.)

3 Prime factorization of 20 is 2 × N × 5.

4 5 is a factor of 110. Right or wrong?

5 Cats: 15, 20, 8 pounds. Dogs: 10, 25, 12 pounds. Highest mean?

7 12000 ml equals ___ L.

10 # = 63 and $ = 9. Find # ÷ $.

11 60 ÷ N = 12

13 A triangle can have a 185° angle. Right or wrong?

14 8/16 = N/100

16 (5,4) is translated 2 left and 3 up. New point: (N,7).

17 Number of ways to choose 1 of 5 colors and 1 of 3 shapes.

19 The measure from the center of a circle to its edge.

20 Compare: 15.5 + 10.5 (more less same) 21.

23 The area of a right triangle with legs 3 and 6.

25 Compare: Area of 3 by 4 rectangle (more less same) area of triangle with base 5 and height 4.

26 1.5 + one half.

27 Chance of rolling the number three on a six-sided die = 1/N.

28 Number of equal sides in an isosceles triangle.

1. Which of the following figures is **not** possible.

   O **A**   A right scalene triangle.

   O **B**   A right equilateral triangle

   O **C**   A trapezoid with one right angle.

   O **D**   A quadrilateral with four congruent sides

2. Angel wants to construct a cylinder from paper shapes. What shapes will she need?

   O **A**   2 circles and 1 rectangle

   O **B**   4 triangles and 1 square

   O **C**   2 squares and 4 rectangles

   O **D**   3 circles and 3 triangles

3. The chart below shows the number of pencils purchased from Mr. Brown's class store during five months last year.

Pencil Sales During Select Months

Month	Pencils Used
July	0
August	15
September	33
November	20
January	30

(a)   During which month was the least number of pencils sold? _____

(b)   Give 2 possible reasons that could explain why different numbers of pencils were sold in different months.

_____

_____

_____

_____

_____

_____

_____

_____

_____

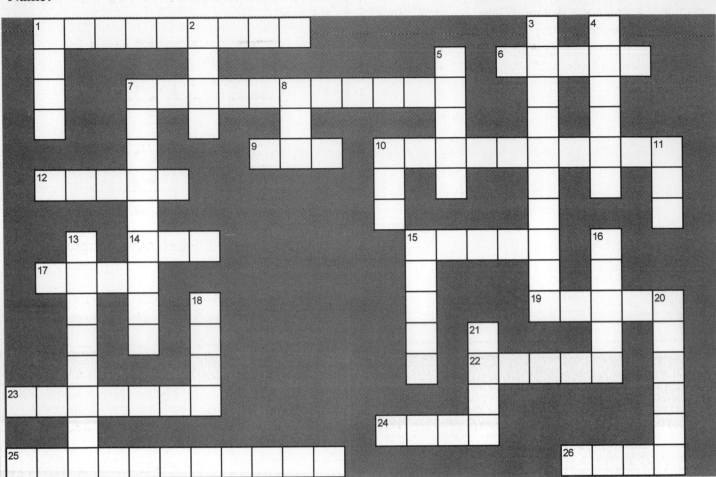

ACROSS

1 Rule: Multiply by 5 and subtract 1. Pattern: 2, 9, N, 219.

6 Rectangle: 28 perimeter, length 6, width ___ .

7 Start with 15. Do this twice: − 5, × 3.

9 A car holds 4 quarts of oil. How many gallons is that?

10 2 tenths = 4 ___ .

12 Number of 30° angles in a right angle.

14 A spinner is split into 3 equal regions numbered 1, 2, and 3. Chance of spinning either a 1 or a 3 = N/3.

15 19 is a factor of 38. Right or wrong?

17 Estimate 63/20 + 25/12 to the nearest unit.

19 The area of a 10 by 12 rectangle is 120. Right or wrong?

22 The mean of 8, 8, and 8.

23 A number that tells the typical value of data in a set.

24 2.7 is plotted to the right of # on number line. Compare: # (more less same) 2.7

25 Tells how big the parts are in a fraction.

26 The Pentagon building in Washington, D.C. has this many sides.

DOWN

1 2 different shirts, 2 different pants. Number of outfits?

2 1 half = N tenths.

3 Small metric measure, about the thickness of a dime.

4 N ÷ 6 = 5

5 4 & N/3 = 19/3

7 Find the prime: 17, 1, 21, 22.

8 15/16 − 5/16 = N/16

10 $0.50 = 1/N dollar.

11 Pattern Machine. Input: 6, 20, 5, 2. Output: 10, 24, 9, N.

13 Perimeter of 5 × 4 rectangle.

15 The plural of radius.

16 A regular octagon has ___ lines of symmetry.

18 Compare: Area of 1 by 2 rectangle (more less same) area of triangle with base 1 and height 2.

20 Recipe uses 2 eggs to make 4 servings. If 24 servings, how many eggs?

21 Compare: 25 − 20.5 (more less same) 5.

1. Darryl had a bag of 7 orange candies, 5 green candies, and 3 red candies. There were no other candies in the bag. Darryl reached in and chose one candy from the bag without looking. What is the probability Darryl selected a green candy?

○ A $\dfrac{12}{15}$ ○ B $\dfrac{5}{15}$

○ C $\dfrac{7}{15}$ ○ D $\dfrac{10}{15}$

2. Felicia is keeping track of how tall her tomato plants grow.

Tomato Growth	
Plant Number	Height (centimeters)
Tomato 1	57.75
Tomato 2	57.52
Tomato 3	57.91
Tomato 4	57.47
Tomato 5	57.23

According to this table, which plant has grown the tallest?

○ A Tomato 1   ○ B Tomato 2
○ C Tomato 3   ○ D Tomato 4

3. Virginia got $35 to spend for her birthday. Below is a chart of all of the items she wants to buy with her money.

Create 2 possible lists of items Virginia could buy that costs at least $30, but not more than $35.

Items Virginia Wants to Buy	
Items	Price
CD	15.75
Jumbo Candy	3.52
Book	5.99
Radio/CD Player	26.47
Purse	9.23

List 1
_____
_____
_____
_____
_____

List 2
_____
_____
_____
_____
_____

Explain your work using words, numbers, or pictures.

"Advice: it's more fun to give than to receive." — Malcolm Forbes, Business Leader

ACROSS

1 N/7 = 5 & 1/7

2 Denominators which are the same are ____ denominators.

4 3/6 (more less same) 2/3.

7 Missing digit: $501.52 × 1.08 = $541.____416

9 The line where a wall meets the floor and where that wall meets the ceiling are ____ lines.

12 Number of 30° angles needed to make 360°.

13 15/16 + 5/16 = N/16

15 A triangle can have a 5° angle. Right or wrong?

16 Number of equal sides in a scalene triangle.

18 The area of a 10 by 12 rectangle is 48. Right or wrong?

20 3.5 + 3/2

21 Pattern: 1, 5, 10, 50, N, 275, 280.

22 2/5 of a Liter is N mL.

23 A line segment connecting any two points on a circle.

25 M = 7. Compare: 42 / M (more less same) 5.

DOWN

1 10 flavors ice cream, 3 flavors of toppings. Choose one each, how many possible desserts?

3 Compare: 16 + 8.57 (more less same) 24.

5 The area of a right triangle with legs 10 and 12.

6 Another word for "reflect".

8 0.700 = N hundredths.

10 32 is divisible by 2. Right or wrong?

11 A way to show data where points are connected with lines. (2 words)

13 38 = N × 19

14 $0.75 = N/20 dollar.

17 Perimeter of 2 × 9 rectangle.

19 Compare: Mean of 5, 5 and 6 (more less same) mean of 3, 6 and 6.

20 Greatest common factor of 12 and 20.

21 (8,6) is translated 3 left and 3 up. New point: (N,9).

22 The mean of 0 and 8.

24 40 ÷ @, if @ = 7 + 1.

1. Which rectangle has an area of 32 square units and a perimeter of 24 units?

A
14
3

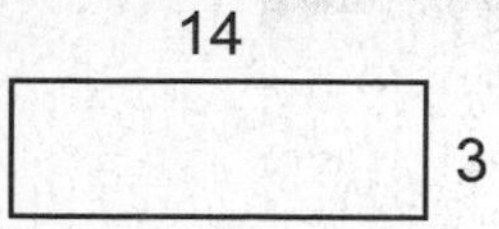

B
6
4

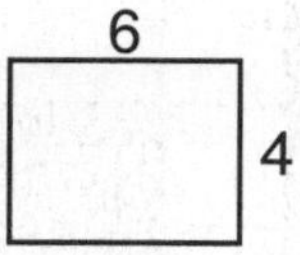

C
8
4

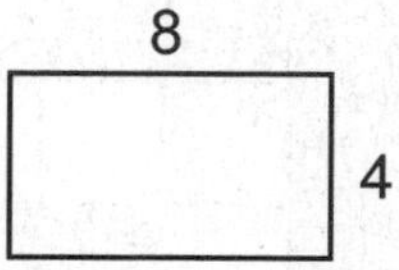

D
16
2

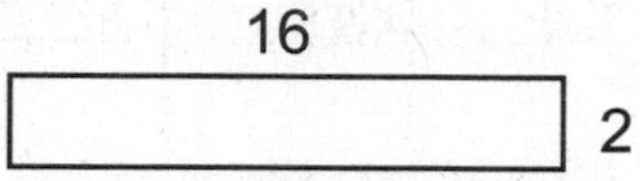

2. Which equation shows the relationship between all of the values in the table below?

x	y
2.5	5
5.0	10
7.5	15
17.5	35

A $y = 2x$

B $x = y + 2$

C $y = x + 2.5$

D $x = 2y + 2.5$

3. Consider the following pattern of figures:

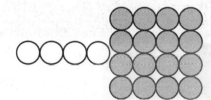

If the pattern continues to grow in the same way, how many circles will be in the next figure?   _____

Sketch a picture of that next figure here:

How many circles would be in the 10th figure?   _____

Explain your answer here:

49

"Well done is better than well said." — Benjamin Franklin, Statesman

/30

ACROSS

1 Start with 7. Do this twice: × 2, − 2.

6 Estimate 89/9 − 50/8 to the nearest unit.

7 Rule: Divide by 2 and add 2. Pattern: 36, 20, 12, N.

8 Chance of rolling the number 5 on a six-sided die = N/6.

9 30/100 + 20/100 = N/100

11 40 pancakes served 12 people. Next week 3 people, about how many pancakes?

13 29 is prime. Right or wrong?

15 Perimeter of square with side length 1.

16 Number of state capitals.

19 8 eighths = N halves.

21 16 ounces.

24 Compare: Mean of 10, 2, 3, 4 (more less same) mean of 0, 10, 5, and 3.

26 A number with many pairs of factors.

27 Compare: Area of 1x2 rectangle (more less same) area of triangle with base 6 and height 1.

DOWN

1 56/16 = 7/N

2 Rectangle: 30 perimeter, width 7, length ___ .

3 The number of years in two decades.

4 21/5 = 4 & N/5.

5 The area of a right triangle with legs 5 and 12.

6 The mean of 50 and 60.

10 Number of right angles in a rectangle.

12 If two fractions are the same size, they're called this.

14 Missing digit: 32.65 × 12.01 = 392.12___5

17 Angle less than 90°.

18 11/2 (more less same) 5.

20 Every triangle has at least one line of symmetry. Right or wrong?

22 1.25 is plotted to the left of # on number line. Compare: # (more less same) 5/4.

23 4 is a factor of 40. Right or wrong?

25 37 ÷ N = 37

28 Pattern Machine. Input: 1, 5, 3, 8. Output: 2, 10, N, 16.

1. DeShawn earned $18.00 on Monday, $12.00 on Tuesday, and then spent $6 on Wednesday. Which number sentence shows how much money DeShawn had left?

○ **A** (18 + 12) – 6 = n

○ **B** (18 + 12) + 6 = n

○ **C** 18 – (12 – 6) = n

○ **D** (18 × 12) – 6 = n

2. What is the area of this figure?

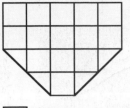

☐ = 1 sq. unit

○ **A** 10 square units
○ **B** 14 square units
○ **C** 15.5 square units
○ **D** 16 square units

3. Joe visits the Ice Cream Emporium every day after school. He orders one scoop of ice cream during each visit. How many days will it take for him to try all possible different combinations of ice cream flavors and cones?

Ice Cream Emporium	
Ice Cream Flavors	Cone Types
Vanilla	Baby
Chocolate	Regular
Bubble Gum	Sugar
Strawberry	Waffle
Cookie Dough	

Explain your work using words, numbers, or pictures.

"It is never too late to become what you might have been." — George Eliot, Author

ACROSS

1 Pattern: 9, 19, 14, 24, 19, 29, N.

6 1/5 (more less same) 4/10.

7 (7,2) is translated 2 right and 1 down. New point: (N,1).

8 0.02 + 10.08 + 5.01 is approximately 15. Right or wrong?

10 Maria's scores: 8, 9, 9. Macky's scores: 8, 8, 9. Who has the greatest mean?

15 The number which is to be divided.

17 Compare: 20 − 1.2 (more less same) 18.

19 The ratio of mass to volume.

20 The measure of two complementary angles, in degrees.

21 $20 = 2 \times 2 \times N$

22 Number of squares that can fit together at one vertex.

24 How much something will hold.

25 Secret Rule: {1, 2, 3, 4} matches {2, N, 6, 8}.

26 A = 10. Compare: A + 10 (more less same) 20.

28 Number of 2 digit numbers less than 15.

29 Least common multiple of 4 and 14.

DOWN

2 Rectangle: 36 perimeter, width 7, length ____ .

3 $0.80 = $N/5

4 In a crossword puzzle, a connected 'across' clue and a 'down' clue form ____ lines.

5 2 is a factor of 300. Right or wrong?

9 The area of a right triangle with legs 10 and 4.

11 Two lines that cross are said to be ____ .

12 A 90° angle is ____ (acute right obtuse).

13 7.5 − 1 & 1/2.

14 Missing digit: $1.35 \times 2.05 =$ 2.___6___5.

16 0.068 = 6 hundredths + N thousandths.

18 @ = 16, ★ = 2. What is @ ÷ ★?

21 8 tenths = N fifths.

23 The perimeter of a 7 by 8 rectangle is 30. Right or wrong?

27 1000 mg = ____ grams.

1. Look at this grid:

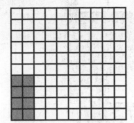

What part of the grid is shaded?

- ○ **A** 8 / 100
- ○ **B** 8 / 10
- ○ **C** 1 / 8
- ○ **D** 1 / 18

2. In the figure below, *QRST* is a parallelogram.

If the area of triangle *QRT* is 18 square inches, what is the area of *QRST*?

- ○ **A** 36 inch^2
- ○ **B** 324 inch^2
- ○ **C** 9 inch^2
- ○ **D** 24 inch^2

3. Ace Construction wants to put a fence around a new swimming pool.

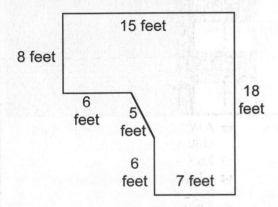

Price of Fencing	
Fencing Type	**Price (per foot)**
Chain Link	15
Tall Wood	13
Short Wood	11
Plastic	18

What is the least amount of fencing he must purchase in order to fence the pool? _____

Ace Construction can spend between $700 and $750 on their fencing.
Which fencing choice, from the chart above, should they make? _____

Explain your answer using words, numbers, or pictures.

ACROSS

2 Pattern: 12, 11, 13, 12, 14, 13, 15, N.

4 Noon is 12:00, but is it a.m. or p.m.?

8 A 125° angle is ___ (acute right obtuse).

9 5 is a factor of 30. Right or wrong?

10 100 ÷ N = 20

11 Rule: Add 2 and divide by 2. Pattern: 22, 12, N.

13 19/8 = N & 3/8

18 41 is divisible by 2. Right or wrong?

19 In the division problem 28 ÷ 7, the number 7 is called the ___ .

20 Half the angle of an equilateral triangle measures N°.

21 Half the angle sum of a triangle (more less same) 90°.

22 Start with 5. Do this 20 times: + 4, − 3.

23 Number of continents.

25 3 halves = N fourths.

26 A regular hexagon is a parallelogram. Right or wrong?

28 3/5 is plotted to the right of # on number line. Compare: # (more less same) 0.6

DOWN

1 Find the composite: 23, 29, 31, 35.

3 Box of 12 costs $12.00. Unit price = N$.

5 Compare: Area of 10 by 25 rectangle (more less same) area of triangle with base 60 and height 8.

6 180° angle is called a ___ angle.

7 6 grams of zinc weighs N mg.

11 Perimeter of square with side length 4.

12 25.998 + 1.002 + 1.988 is approximately what integer?

14 7/20 + 5/20 = N/20

15 Secret Rule: {12, 14, 7, 10} matches {6, 8, 1, N}.

16 A geometric object that goes on forever in both directions.

17 The mean of 8 and 24.

23 8/2 = 24/N

24 Rectangle: 6 perimeter, width 1, length ___ .

27 Chance of rolling the number six on a six-sided die = N/6.

1. What is 7/8 written as a percent?

    ○ **A** 7.8 %

    ○ **B** 70 %

    ○ **C** 87.5 %

    ○ **D** 50 %

2. Look at the two rectangles below.

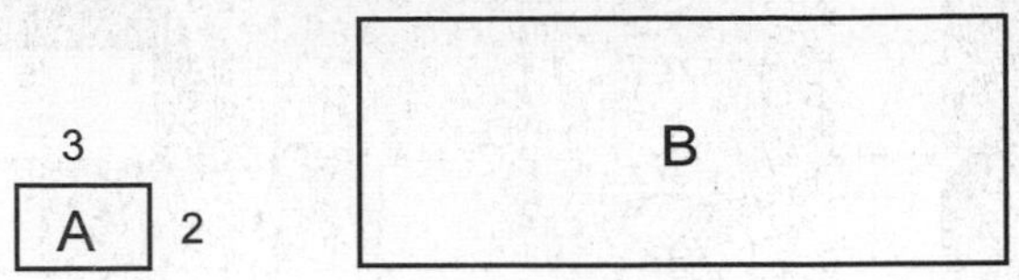

If each side of rectangle A is multiplied by 5 to make rectangle B, how does the area of rectangle B compare to the area of rectangle A?

    ○ **A** B is 6 times as large

    ○ **B** B is 25 times as large

    ○ **C** B is 5 times as large

    ○ **D** B is 15 times as large

3. Zoe, Hana, and Debbie each ride to the library on their bikes.

    • Zoe rides her bike *b* miles.

    • Hana rides her bike 2 times as many miles as Zoe does.

    • Debbie rides her bike 3 more miles than Zoe does.

Use *b* to write an expression for the number of miles Hana rides her bike.

Use *b* to write an expression for the number of miles Debbie rides her bike.

ACROSS

2 In probability, a trial where you don't know the outcome.

5 An acute angle can be 90°. Right or wrong?

7 Rule: Multiply by 3 and subtract 2. Pattern: 2, 4, N, 28.

8 5/4 (more less same) 5/6.

10 3 different shirts, 4 different pants. Number of outfits?

11 Pattern: 20, 10, 18, 9, N, 8, 14.

12 7000 mg makes ___ grams.

14 The perimeter of a 1 by 2 rectangle is 2. Right or wrong?

15 If & = 2, what is 100 ÷ & ?

18 Corn stalks in a field are roughly ___ lines.

19 Find the prime: 6, 1, 61, 16.

21 A "piece of line" which has two endpoints.

24 The area of a right triangle with legs 7 and 2.

25 Compare: 16 – 8.5 (more less same) 7.

26 B = 16. Compare: B – 7 (more less same) 8.

27 A regular octagon is a parallelogram. Right or wrong?

28 (1,7) is translated 2 right and 2 down. New point: (3,N).

DOWN

1 2 is a factor of 55. Right or wrong?

3 0.021 = N/1000

4 Prime factorization of 25 is N × N.

6 A 2D figure that appears the same in a mirror has a line of ___ .

7 $0.15 = 3/N dollar.

9 Number of hexagons that can fit together at one vertex.

13 A set of points all the same distance from a given point.

16 Least common multiple of 5 and 15.

17 0.25 × 20

18 2000 of these make a ton.

20 0.75 + one-fourth.

22 Compare: Mean of 12 and 8 (more less same) mean of 13 and 7.

23 Missing digit: 15.10 × 5.05 = 76.___55

1. Which angle is approximately 90 degrees?

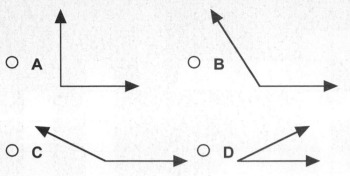

○ **A** ○ **B** ○ **C** ○ **D**

2. Maurice skated with his two friends on Saturday. He skated with Mark for 3/4 of an hour and with Ian for 2/3 of an hour. How much time did Maurice spend skating?

○ **A** $1\frac{3}{4}$ hours ○ **B** $1\frac{5}{12}$ hours

○ **C** 2 hours ○ **D** $2\frac{1}{12}$ hours

3. Mr. Perry is tracking the students in his after school club who do volunteer work each year.

Volunteer Hours	
Person	Number of Hours
Samantha	22
Tyrone	11
Chen	15
Donte	28

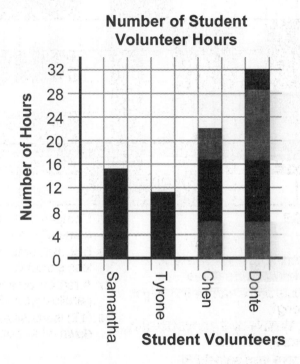

Number of Student Volunteer Hours

Mr. Perry made a graph of the information listed on the chart. Unfortunately, he was not a careful worker, and many of the pieces of information on the graph are incorrect.

Which students have the incorrect number of volunteer hours recorded on the graph? Explain.

_____

_____

_____

_____

"Obstacles are things a person sees when he takes his eyes off the goal." — E. Joseph Cossman, Salesman

/35

ACROSS

4 Find the composite: 40, 41, 43, 47.

8 Angle in a square (more less same) angle in an equilateral triangle.

11 Two data points, such as (3,2), is an ____ pair.

13 7 is a factor of 54. Right or wrong?

14 Rectangle: 10 area, width 2, length N.

15 Compare: A number plotted to the right of 2/3 on a number line (more less same) 2/3.

18 The two line segments that make the letter 'T' are ____ lines.

20 The middle of a circle.

23 20×0.5

26 The area of a right triangle with legs 5 and 4.

27 A cat supposedly has this many lives.

28 A record of data, made by making small marks.

31 The perimeter of a 1 by 2 rectangle is 6. Right or wrong?

32 Two sides in a triangle can be parallel. Right or wrong?

33 One unit of vitamin weighs 350 mg. Grams in 200 units?

DOWN

1 Pattern Machine. Input: 1, 5, 12, 18. Output: 0, N, 11, 17.

2 M = 10. Compare: 90 / M (more less same) 9.

3 4/5 (more less same) 2/10.

5 Rule: Subtract 2 and double. Pattern: 10, 16, N, 52.

6 Compare: 3 + 12.95 (more less same) 15.

7 1 tenth = N hundredths.

9 Start with 0. Do this 100 times: + 7, − 6.

10 1 fourth = N eighths.

12 A quotient is the result of this operation.

14 A spinner is split into 10 equal regions numbered 1-10. Chance of spinning odd number = N/10.

15 Compare: Mean of 8, 5 and 7 (more less same) mean of 6, 6 and 6.

16 $0.50 = N/20 dollar.

17 32 fluid ounces is one of these.

19 3 cats weigh 20 pounds. 12 cats weigh N pounds.

21 10.648 + 2.989 − 0.5 is approximately what integer?

22 8 flavors ice cream, 2 flavors of toppings. Choose one each, how many possible desserts?

24 Missing digit: $943.425 \div 10.5 =$ 89.____5

25 Greatest common factor of 18 and 24.

29 Compare: Area of triangle with base 5 and height 6 (more less same) area of triangle with base 2 and height 16.

30 $48 \div N = 8$

1. The chart below shows the number of games played by each division in the city's soccer league.

Soccer Leagues	Number of Games Played
North Division	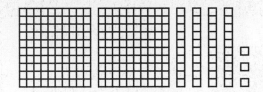
South Division	
East Division	
West Division	

⚽ = 4 games

How many games were played all together?

○ **A**   16.5   ○ **B**   72

○ **C**   34   ○ **D**   66

2. Look at the place value rods below.

Key: = 1

What number is represented by the rods?

○ **A**   2430

○ **B**   342

○ **C**   24.3

○ **D**   2.43

3. Look at the factor tree below.

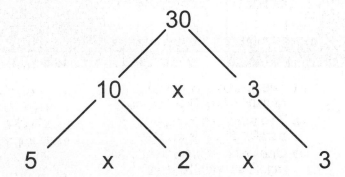

Draw a similar factor tree for 350 using multiplication.

ACROSS

3 Rectangle: 12 area, width 4, length N.

4 50 pancakes served 18 people. Next week 9 people, about how many pancakes?

7 Angle in a regular pentagon (more less same) right angle.

9 $45 = 3 \times 3 \times N$

11 One sample of ore weighs 1290 g, another weighs 2710 g. How many kg do the two samples weigh together?

12 Area of 2×3 rectangle.

14 Greatest common factor of 18 and 81.

15 $90.2 - 60.2$

19 $2 g = \underline{\quad}$ mg.

20 A right angle must be 90°. Right or wrong?

21 R = 5. Compare: $15 + R$ (more less same) 20.

23 (1,7) is translated 2 right and 2 up. New point: (N,9).

25 An eight-sided polygon.

27 Start with 100. Do this 75 times: + 4, − 5.

29 A polygon with 7 sides has this many angles.

30 The two line segments in an addition symbol are _____ lines.

32 Estimate $111/10 - 61/6$ to the nearest unit.

33 $9/100 + 9/100 = N/100$

DOWN

1 The mean of 60 and 80.

2 Tool for measuring angles.

5 Pattern: N, 10, 20, 19, 38, 37, 74, 73, 146.

6 Compare: A number plotted to the left of 2/3 on a number line (more less same) 2/3.

8 9 thirds = N halves.

10 2 is a factor of 36. Right or wrong?

13 Polygon with angle sum of 180°.

15 N/5 dollar = 40 cents.

16 $37/6 = 6 \& N/6$.

17 How many possible dinners if you choose 1 each of: 2 entrees, 4 vegetables?

18 Starting at the end and figuring things out in reverse is called working _____ .

22 The perimeter of a 10 by 12 rectangle is 22. Right or wrong?

24 Shape of a yield sign.

26 Pattern Machine. Input: 1, 4, 3, 6. Output: 3, 12, N, 18.

27 Number of thousandths in 0.012.

28 5/6 (more less same) 5/4.

31 $50 \div [\,]$, if $[\,] = 5$.

1. Centerville had a record amount of snow one week in November.

Days of Week	Centimeters of Snow
Sunday	10.2
Monday	16.8
Tuesday	10.04
Wednesday	14.08
Thursday	22.6
Friday	22.07
Saturday	16.89

Using the information from the chart above, put the days of the week in order according to amount of snowfall, from most to least.

○ A Tuesday, Sunday, Wednesday, Monday, Saturday, Friday, Thursday

○ B Sunday, Tuesday, Wednesday, Saturday, Monday, Thursday, Friday

○ C Friday, Thursday, Sunday, Monday, Wednesday, Tuesday, Saturday

○ D Thursday, Friday, Saturday, Monday, Wednesday, Sunday, Tuesday

2. Look at the figure below.

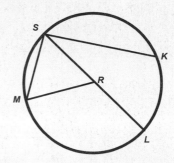

Which of the following line segments is the diameter of the circle?

○ A $\overline{SL}$

○ B $\overline{SK}$

○ C $\overline{SM}$

○ D $\overline{MR}$

3. Ariel needs a box to hold exactly 30 brownies for her teacher. Plan how the brownies will be placed in the box so that the box is full, with no spaces left over. Show your work in the space provided below.

"If opportunity doesn't knock, build a door." — Milton Berle, Comedian

/35

ACROSSZ

1 1/6 (more less same) 1/5.

6 The measure of an angle of a regular pentagon in degrees.

11 Compare: Area of triangle with base 2 and height 6 (more less same) area of triangle with base 3 and height 4.

12 Jamal's scores: 46, 47, 48. Jenny's scores: 40, 45, 50. Who has the greatest mean?

16 7.25 + three-fourths.

17 Area of 4 × 3 rectangle.

18 Find the prime: 9, 19, 33, 57.

19 The mean of 8, 9 and 10.

20 The area of a right triangle with legs 2 and 3.

21 Use this to find something's weight.

22 An eight-slice pizza weighs 2 kg. Grams in 1 slice = 200 + N.

24 A 130° angle is split into two smaller angles. Both new angles must be acute. Right or wrong?

25 I am a multiple of 15 and 9. I am less than 50.

27 2 is a factor of 16. Right or wrong?

29 Rule: Double and add 2. Pattern: 0, 2, 6, N.

30 Start with 25. Do this 10 times: +2, -4.

31 Tails comes up on a coin flip about N times out of 20.

32 Missing digit: 15.25 × 4.20 = 64.___5

DOWN

2 Two figures which are the same shape but not necessarily the same size are ____ .

3 @ = 14, ★ = 7. What is @ ÷ ★?

4 Prime factorization of 27 is $N \times N \times N$.

5 Compare: A number plotted to the left of 3.75 on a number line (more less same) 3.75.

7 (1,7) is translated 2 right and 2 up. New point: (3,N).

8 3/8 = N/32

9 Shape of a speed limit sign.

10 A quadrilateral with two pairs of parallel sides.

13 11 & 1/5 = N/5.

14 3 is a factor of 14. Right or wrong?

15 Pattern: 7, 13, 11, 17, 15, 21, 19, N.

21 70 ÷ N = 10

23 The place to the right of the decimal point tells how many of these.

24 A triangle can have two right angles. Right or wrong?

25 0.095 = 9 hundredths + N thousandths.

26 11/12 − 7/12 = N/12

28 Grams in 1/100 kg.

1. Which number sentence is true for all pairs of values shown in the table below?

Input	Output
M	*P*
48	8
12	2
24	4
30	5

○ **A** M − 40 = P   ○ **B** M ÷ 6 = P

○ **C** P + 20 = M   ○ **D** M ÷ 8 = P

2. In the figure below, *LMNO* is a parallelogram.

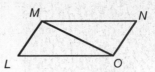

If the area of triangle *LMO* is 12 square inches, what is the area of *LMNO*?

○ **A**   144 square inches

○ **B**   48 square inches

○ **C**   32 Square inches

○ **D**   24 square inches

3. Aaron did a survey of his classmates to determine what community service project the class should do in the spring. The data he collected is summarized here.

Trail restoration: 4   Litter removal: 3

Crafts for elderly: 5   Food bank collection: 12

Using the information, create a bar chart on the grid. Be sure to:

• Title the chart
• Label the axes
• Graph all the data
• Use an appropriate scale

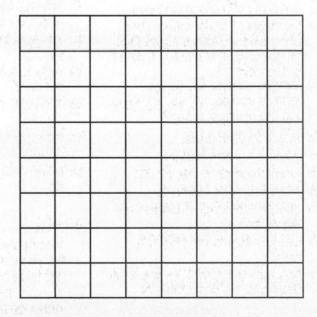

"To be upset over what you don't have is to waste what you do have." — Ken S. Keyes, Jr., Author

ACROSS

4 6 × 1.5

7 A square is translated. One vertex goes from (2,2) to (3,5), another goes from (2,4) to (3,N).

9 Missing digit: 79.8 ÷ 9.5 = 8.____

11 A row of telephone poles form roughly ____ line segments.

12 Compare: 9.1 + 1.9 (more less same) 10.

15 The area of a right triangle with legs 3 and 12.

17 # = 81 and $ = 9. Find # ÷ $.

18 Secret Rule: {7, 6, 5, 10} matches {9, 8, N, 12}.

19 4/5 (more less same) 10/2.

20 11/22 = 4/N

22 Chance of rolling a number greater than 2 on a six-sided die = N/6.

23 A fraction whose numerator is greater than its denominator.

25 Value of "1" in 54.010 = 1 ____ …

27 Rectangle: 30 area, width 6, length N.

28 Number of ways to choose 1 of 3 colors and 1 of 2 shapes.

29 6 halves = N fourths.

31 35 ÷ N = 7

32 Find the composite: 53, 56, 59, 61.

34 Compare: Area of triangle with base 7 and height 2 (more less same) area of triangle with base 3 and height 4.

DOWN

1 A whole number and fraction together make a ____ number.

2 The dot between the ones and the tenths.

3 Usually measured in square units.

5 5 is a factor of 52. Right or wrong?

6 A soup can is this shape.

8 22 = 2 × N

10 The area of a triangle with B = 5 and H = 10 is 50. Right or wrong?

13 Rule: Divide by 2 and subtract 2. Pattern: 100, 48, 22, N.

14 3/4 dollars = N cents.

16 8.005 + 14.898 + 2.023 is approximately what integer?

21 Greatest common factor of 9 and 15.

22 5000 g makes N kg.

24 A quadrilateral can have two right angles. Right or wrong?

26 Cats: 7, 19, 14 pounds. Dogs: 20, 15, 8 pounds. Highest mean?

30 F = 7. Compare: 6 × F (more less same) 49.

33 1.625 + three-eighths.

1. Anna needs to build a pen to house her new chickens. The width of the pen is half the length.

width = 8 feet

How much fencing will Anna need to go around the perimeter of her new pen?

○ **A** 23 feet   ○ **B** 48 feet

○ **C** 16 feet   ○ **D** 40 feet

2. Which angle is approximately 30 degrees?

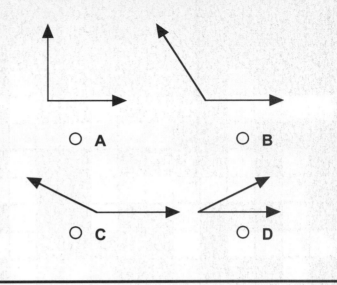

○ **A**   ○ **B**

○ **C**   ○ **D**

3. Rory is thinking of a mystery shape. He gives the following clues:

- It is an polygon.
- It is a quadrilateral.
- It has two sides which are parallel.
- It has exactly two right angles.
- All the sides are different lengths.

In the space below, sketch Rory's mystery shape. Explain how your shape matches with Rory's clues.

ACROSS

3 12 is a factor of 28. Right or wrong?

5 Estimate 49/8 + 82/9 to the nearest unit.

7 Greek geometer, 300 BCE, the "father of geometry".

9 How hot or cold something is.

10 Missing digit: 62.3 × 12.03 = 749.4___9

11 A game where all players have an equal chance.

14 18.2 − 11/5

16 A triangle can have three acute angles. Right or wrong?

18 Rule: Multiply by 3 and subtract 1. Pattern: 4, 11, N, 95.

20 How wide something is.

24 The area of a right triangle with legs 4 and 2.

25 5 different shirts, 2 different pants. Number of outfits?

27 Angle in an equilateral triangle (more less same) right angle.

29 Literally translated, "rectangle" means "___ angle".

30 Compare: A number plotted to the right of 1.4 on a number line (more less same) 7/5.

31 B = 16. Compare: 18 − B (more less same) 2.

32 Recipe uses 3 eggs to make 6 servings. If 18 servings, how many eggs?

33 Compare: Area of triangle with base 10 and height 1 (more less same) area of triangle with base 3 and height 4.

DOWN

1 Pattern Machine. Input: 7, 12, 9, 10. Output: 2, 7, 4, N.

2 1 half = N fourteenths.

4 Start with 0. Do this 50 times: + 8, − 6.

6 An enormous chocolate bunny weighs 17,000 grams. How many kg of chocolate is that?

8 Compare: 50 − 25.5 (more less same) 25.

11 Find factors with a ___ tree.

12 The area of a triangle with B = 5 and H = 10 is 25. Right or wrong?

13 $0.25 = 1/N dollar.

14 Least common multiple of 10 and 12.

15 Find the prime: 52, 1, 41, 4.

17 N ÷ 4 = 3

19 12 twentieths = 6 ___ .

21 A spinner is split into 3 equal regions numbered 1, 2, and 3. Chance of spinning a number less than three = N/3.

22 3/2 (more less same) 2/3.

23 The flagpoles outside of the United Nations building are ___ line segments.

26 Rectangle: 30 area, width 5, length N.

28 Compare: Mean of 0 and 5 (more less same) mean of 2 and 3.

1. A fraction of this group of circles is shaded.

Which of the following groups is shaded to show the fraction with the same value?

○ A

○ B

○ C

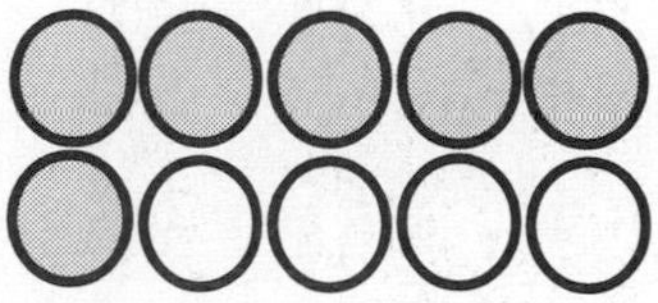

○ D

2. The custodian at Beach Elementary School must order supplies for their new playground area. For which of the following would he need to know the area of the play area?

○ A   Determining how high the swing set should be set

○ B   Determining how much grass seed is needed to fill the space

○ C   Determining how many feet of fencing are needed to go around the area

○ D   Determining how many children will fit on the play structure at one time

3. Look at the number pattern below:

$$1, 4, 9, 16, 25, \ldots$$

What are the next two numbers in the number pattern? Write your answer on the lines below.

_____ , _____

Explain the rule you used to find the next two numbers in the pattern in the space provided below.

"Even if you're on the right track, you'll get run over if you just sit there." — Will Rogers, Humorist

ACROSS

1 4.8 + one-fifth.

5 Number of right angles needed to make 450°.

6 Prime factorization of 28 is 2 × 2 × N.

11 0.003 = N thousandths.

12 12/15 + 3/15 = N

13 Grams in 25,000 mg.

14 300 is divisible by 2. Right or wrong?

17 3 cats weigh 40 pounds. 6 cats weigh N pounds.

18 A square is translated. One vertex goes from (4,5) to (3,5), another goes from (2,3) to (1,N).

19 N/8 = 2 & 1/8.

23 3 feet.

26 5 flavors ice cream, 3 flavors of toppings. Choose one each, how many possible desserts?

27 Greatest common factor of 18 and 36.

28 A 3D figure with a polygon base connected to sides that meet at a point.

30 M = 16. Compare: 32 / M (more less same) 3.

31 Compare: 65.5 + 5.5 (more less same) 70.

32 Rectangle: 4 area, length 1, width N.

DOWN

2 A number which has no remainder when divided by 2.

3 Literally means "for every hundred".

4 The area of a triangle with B = 1 and H = 2 is 2. Right or wrong?

5 The mean of 3, 3 and 9.

7 Area of 2 × 6 rectangle.

8 A vertical line and a horizontal line are ___ lines.

9 One sheet of parchment weighs 3 grams. If a ream is 2000 sheets, how heavy is a ream of parchment in kg?

10 Pattern: 3, 9, 10, 30, N, 93, 94.

11 1 fourth = N twelfths.

13 $0.40 = N/50 dollar.

15 0.489 + 2.989 − 0.45 is approximately what integer?

16 49 ÷ @, if @ = 5 + 2.

20 A coin is this 3-D shape.

21 Pattern Machine. Input: 2, 9, 10, 20. Output: 9, N, 17, 27.

22 Start with 105. Do this 100 times: + 4, − 5.

24 A protractor measures these.

25 Compare: A number plotted to the left of 1.4 on a number line (more less same) 7/5.

29 A 70° angle can be combined with another angle to form a right angle. Right or wrong?

Parent/Gaurdian signature: For puzzle time, return on:

1. Which of the following have at least two sides that appear to be perpendicular?

○ **A**

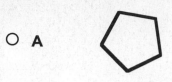

○ **B**

○ **C**

○ **D**

2. Billy ate 3 times as many pizza slices as Alex. If *S* represents the number pieces eaten by Billy, which expression can be used to find the number of pieces of pizza eaten by Alex?

○ **A** $S + 3$

○ **B** $S \div 3$

○ **C** $S - 3$

○ **D** $S \times 3$

3. Look at the number sentence below.

$436 = \triangle$ hundreds + 22 tens + $\square$ ones.

Find one number for $\triangle$ and one number for $\square$ that make the number sentence true. Show your work in the space provided below.

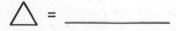

$\triangle$ = _____ $\square$ = _____

"The man who makes no mistakes does not usually make anything." — W.C. Magee, Bishop

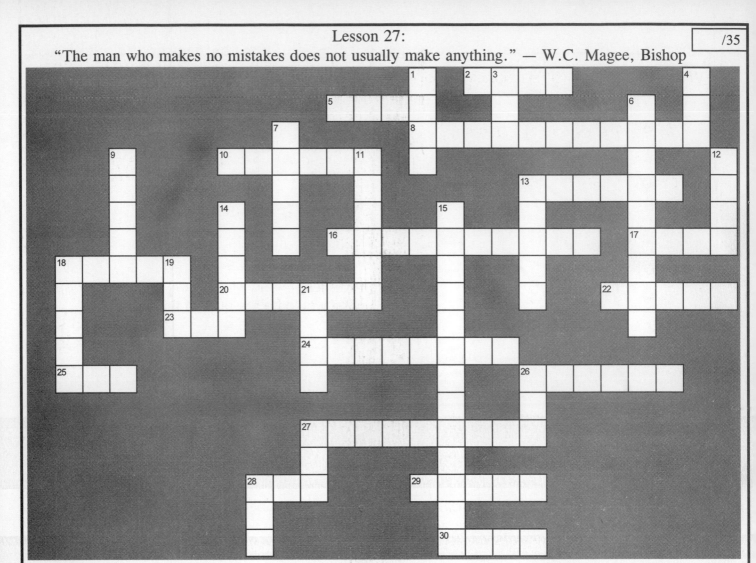

ACROSS

2 Missing digit: 71.33 × 3.71 = 264.63___3

5 Compare: Mean of 5, 6, 7, 8 (more less same) mean of 2, 10, 10, and 4.

8 25/100 + 50/100 = N/100

10 A measure of length, from the bottom to the top.

13 The area of a right triangle with legs 4 and 15.

16 N, 50, 60, 30, 40, 20, 30, 15, 25.

17 30 = 2 × 3 × N

18 97 is prime. Right or wrong?

20 The mean of 10, 20 and 30.

22 Volume is usually measured in ___ units.

23 31 ÷ N = 31

24 A number less than zero is ___?.

25 A right isosceles triangle has this many 45° angles.

26 40/60 = 8/N

27 Twenty − 9/3.

28 Rule: Divide by 2 and add 2. Pattern: 20, 12, 8, N.

29 A triangle with a 30° angle must be acute. Right or wrong?

30 Compare: A number plotted to the left of 6/8 on a number line (more less same) 0.75

DOWN

1 7/2 (more less same) 4.

3 21/5 = 4 & N/5.

4 A square is translated. One vertex goes from (4,5) to (3,5), another goes from (2,3) to (N,3).

6 Number of thousandths in 0.064.

7 2 is a factor of 500. Right or wrong?

9 4 is a factor of 42. Right or wrong?

11 Area of 5 × 4 rectangle.

12 Compare: Area of triangle with B = 5 and H = 10 (more less same) area of rectangle with L = 2 and W = 12.

13 1 cake served 9 people. Next week 27 people, about how many cakes?

14 At 2 o'clock a clock's hands form which angle: acute, right, or obtuse?

15 A four-sided figure.

18 2.7 centimeters is longer than 25 mm. Right or wrong?

19 2000 milligrams is ___ grams.

21 A stitch in time saves how many?

26 Start with 160. Do this 75 times: + 6, − 8.

27 Chance of rolling the number 4 on a six-sided die = 1/N.

28 18 ÷ [], if [] = 3.

1. Which would result in the largest number?

     ○ **A**   7 squared + 3 squared

     ○ **B**   7 cubed

     ○ **C**   7 × 21 × 28

     ○ **D**   10 squared

2. Look at the shaded figure below.

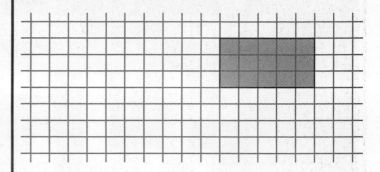

If the length and width of the figure were doubled, what would be the area of the figure?

     ○ **A**   15 square units
     ○ **B**   34 square units
     ○ **C**   46 square units
     ○ **D**   60 square units

3. The campers at Lakeshore Camp have a contest each week to have the cleanest cabin. The chart below shows the number of clean cabin wins awarded to each cabin during the year.

How many more wins did Cabin Three have then Cabin One?
Explain your answer using words, numbers, or pictures.

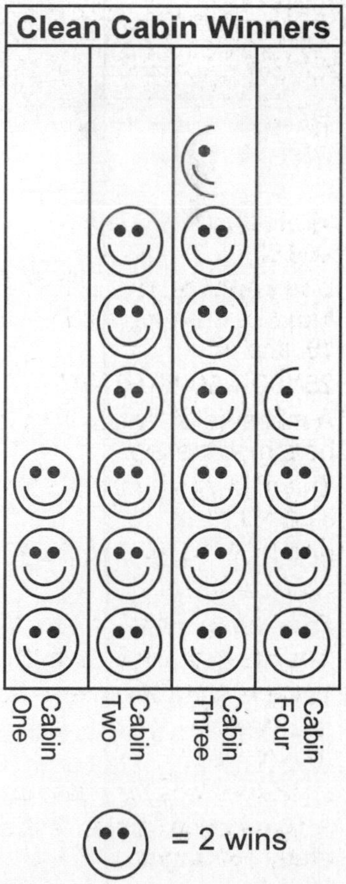

_____

_____

_____

_____

_____

_____

_____

_____

_____

Clean Cabin Winners

Cabin One	Cabin Two	Cabin Three	Cabin Four

😊 = 2 wins

"Imagination is more important than knowledge." — Einstein, Physicist

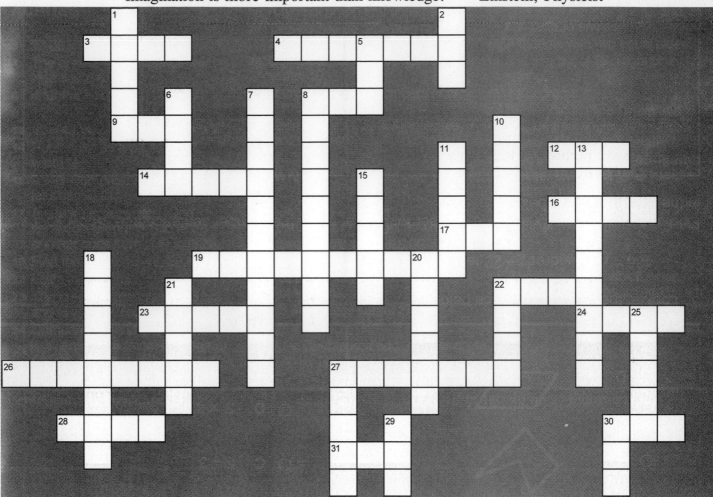

ACROSS

3 $0.05 = $N/100

4 The area of a right triangle with legs 5 and 6.

8 4 tenths = N fifths.

9 1/2 + 0.5 + one-half + 0.500.

12 @ = 42, ★ = 7. What is @ ÷ ★?

14 Rectangle: 35 area, length 5, width N.

16 A = 6. Compare: A + 16 (more less same) 21.

17 A square is translated. One vertex goes from (1,1) to (3,5), another goes from (1,6) to (3,N).

19 Find the prime: 15, 46, 29, 9.

22 Liters in 5000 mL.

23 The area of a triangle with B = 3 and H = 4 is 7. Right or wrong?

24 Compare: Area of triangle with B = 10 and H = 5 (more less same) area of rectangle with L = 8 and W = 4.

26 A type of graph that uses bars.

27 Tails comes up on a coin flip about N times out of 30.

28 Compare: 12.5 – 2.5 (more less same) 10.

30 Number of 4 digit numbers (< or = 1000).

31 Secret Rule: {1, 2, 3, 4} matches {N, 20, 30, 40}.

DOWN

1 0.95 + 1.95 + 3.95 is approximately 7. Right or wrong?

2 Missing digit: 10.20 × 8.05 = 82.___1

5 0.022 = 2 hundredths + N thousandths.

6 2/5 (more less same) 2/10.

7 4/7 = N/49

8 Rule: Double and add 2. Pattern: 1, 4, 10, N.

10 70 = 2 × 5 × N

11 This word means "sharp" and can refer to angles.

13 A triangle with two equal sides.

15 3 is a factor of 28. Right or wrong?

18 1000 grams.

20 Perpendicular lines meet at a ___ degree angle.

21 A way of displaying data.

22 Fred's scores: 12, 12, 15. Fawn's scores: 13, 14, 16. Who has the greatest mean?

25 77 ÷ N = 11

27 Least common multiple of 8 and 10.

29 5/8 + 0.375

30 A whole number which when divided by two has an odd bit left over.

1. Chelsey has two spinners.

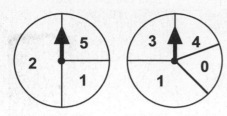

She spins each arrow once and writes down the sum of the two numbers. How many different sums are possible?

O **A** 4   O **B** 7

O **C** 8   O **D** 12

2. Which list contains only prime numbers?

O **A** 1, 5, 9, 17, 21

O **B** 1, 3, 5, 8, 19

O **C** 3, 7, 11, 13, 17

O **D** 7, 11, 13, 15, 19

3. Jasmine needs to make enough valentines for all of the residents at Sunnydale Retirement Center. There are 12 residents on each of the 8 floors at Sunnydale.

Jasmine plans on working for 9 nights, making 10 valentines each night.

Will she have enough valentines to give one to each resident? Explain how you know using the space provided below.

ACROSS

1 Greatest common factor of 14 and 21.

3 A way to show data using rectangles.

7 Compare: 8.2 + 10 (more less same) 18.

8 The area of a triangle with B = 3 and H = 4 is 6. Right or wrong?

12 A rhombus with right angles.

13 Secret Rule: {4, 12, 9, 15} matches {1, N, 6, 12}.

16 Cats: 12, 12, 8 pounds. Dogs: 15, 15, 4 pounds. Highest mean?

17 Separates units from fractions in a decimal number.

18 1.75 – 5/4

19 Chance of rolling a number less than 3 on a six-sided die = N/6.

20 4.001 + 6.003 + 5.988 is approximately what integer?

25 63 ÷ N = 7

27 8 is a factor of 25. Right or wrong?

28 Start with 25. Do this 20 times: + 8, – 9.

29 11.4 – two-fifths.

30 The number 0.5 units to the right of 7.5 on the number line.

31 Number of times that parallel lines cross.

33 Find the composite: 51, 53, 31, 13.

DOWN

1 Compare: Area of triangle with B = 3 and H = 4 (more less same) area of rectangle with L = 2 and W = 3.

2 A quantity whose value can change.

4 6/12 = 7/N

5 F = 10. Compare: 10 × F (more less same) 100.

6 2/3 (more less same) 4/3.

9 Missing digit: 230.04 ÷ 14.2 = 16.___

10 A polygon with N sides also has N ___ .

11 If your sister's foot is 120 mm long, how many centimeters long is it?

14 6/4 dollars = 1 dollars and N cents.

15 1000 meters.

20 Number of ways to choose 1 of 4 colors and 1 of 4 shapes.

21 Small number written above and to the right of a number to show repeated multiplication.

22 Rectangle: 35 area, length 7, width N.

23 Rule: Divide by 2 and subtract 2. Pattern: 40, 18, N.

24 Box of 9 costs $4.50. Unit price = N¢.

26 The area of a right triangle with legs 5 and 8.

32 5 halves = N fourths.

1. What is the area of this figure?

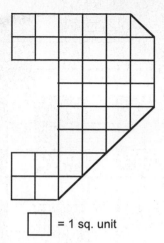

☐ = 1 sq. unit

○ **A**   29.5 square units

○ **B**   30.5 square units

○ **C**   31.5 square units

○ **D**   42 square units

2. Rosalita used the equation $y = x \div 4$ to fill in the table below.

x	y
12	3
24	6
40	10
52	—

What number completes the table?

○ **A**   13   ○ **B**   15

○ **C**   16   ○ **D**   17

3. Kevin packed books in a box to send to the library. He packed each box:

2 books long
2 books wide
13 book high

How many books does each box hold? Show your work in the space provided below.

ACROSS

2 The area of a triangle with B = 3 and H = 4 is 12. Right or wrong?

6 Estimate 56/57 + 45/46 to the nearest unit.

7 Area of rectangle = 5 sq. cm. L = 5 cm, W = ___ cm.

8 A group of numbers related by an operation, such as 7, 8, and 15, is called a ___ family.

10 28 = 2 × 2 × N

12 At 9 o'clock a clock's hands form which angle: acute, right, or obtuse?

14 The number 0.5 units to the left of 7.5 on the number line.

19 Metric unit meaning literally "100 measures".

20 5 different shirts, 3 different pants. Number of outfits?

21 Pattern Machine. Input: 15, 2, 12, 17. Output: 18, 5, N, 20.

23 0.048 = N/1000

25 Least common multiple of 15 and 9.

26 B = 10. Compare: 10 – B (more less same) 1.

29 A square is cut along the diagonal. The two triangles are acute. Right or wrong?

31 Expressing a number as a decimal times a power of 10 is ___ notation.

33 The 'Creemy-D' candy bar is 5.5 cm wide. How wide is it in millimeters?

DOWN

1 2 is a factor of 39. Right or wrong?

3 1000 mg = N grams.

4 A pair of numbers which tell a location on a map.

5 1 half = N eighths.

9 $0.60 = 6/N dollar.

11 12 & N/5 = 68/5.

13 6/15 – 3/15 = N/15

14 If & = 1, what is 70 ÷ & ?

15 Tells what distances on a map represent.

16 A square is translated. One vertex goes from (7,2) to (3,5), another goes from (5,4) to (N,7).

17 Recipe uses 3 eggs to make 10 servings. If 20 servings, how many eggs?

18 Pattern 50, 25, 26, 13, 14, N, 8.

20 The mean of 2, 8, and 20.

22 Start with 2. Do this 50 times: + 2, – 1.

24 A 3D box shape is known as a rectangular ___ .

27 11/4 – 2.75

28 Triangle: 24 area, height 8, base ___ .

30 Line A and line B are both perpendicular to line Q. Right or wrong: Lines A and B are parallel.

32 Compare: 12.5 – 6.5 (more less same) 6.

1. The score at the end of the first half of the Hawks-Lions rematch game is shown below.

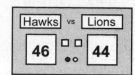

In the second half, the Hawks scored 22 points and the Lions scored 39 points. What was the score at the end of the game?

○ **A** Hawks: 85, Lions: 66

○ **B** Hawks: 70, Lions: 83

○ **C** Hawks: 83 Lions: 70

○ **D** Hawks: 68, Lions: 83

2. Colin played chess with his three friends after school. He played with Mark for 5/6 of an hour, Allison for 1/2 an hour and with Morgan for 2/3 of an hour. How much time did Colin spend playing?

○ **A** $1\frac{1}{2}$ hours

○ **B** $1\frac{11}{12}$ hours

○ **C** $2\frac{1}{4}$ hours

○ **D** 2 hours

3. Janell went to the grocery store for her grandma. She bought eggs for $1.19, 2 apples for $0.43 each, and a box of cereal for $3.50. If Janell pays with a $10 bill, how much change will she receive? Show your work in the space provided below.

"In order to achieve anything, you must be brave enough to fail." — Kirk Douglas, Actor

ACROSS

1 1/5 (more less same) 2/10.

8 $0.90 = N/20 dollar.

11 Compare: 18.5 + 2.5 (more less same) 21.

14 Start with 135. Do this 100 times: + 5, − 6.

16 Greatest common factor of 22 and 33.

17 Compare: Area of triangle with B = 1 and H = 14 (more less same) area of rectangle with L = 2 and W = 3.

18 Roll up a rectangle and put a circle on the top and bottom. What is it?

20 N/8 = 3 & 2/8.

22 A spinner is split into 10 equal regions numbered 1-10. Chance of spinning a number divisible by 2 = N/10.

24 Rule: Subtract 2 and double. Pattern: 7, 10, 16, N.

28 The area of an equilateral triangle with one side = 4 is 8. Right or wrong?

29 A fraction that relates rates.

32 3 eighths = N eightieths.

35 Small unit of length in the U.S., about 2.5 cm.

36 Line C and line D are both perpendicular to line X. Lines C and D are perpendicular to each other. Right or wrong?

37 Find the composite: 67, 47, 37, 57.

39 At 7 o'clock a clock's hands form which angle: acute, right, or obtuse?

DOWN

2 Midnight is 12:00. But is it a.m. or p.m.?

3 Area of rectangle = 16 sq. cm. L = 2 cm, W = ____ cm.

4 Eighths in 0.375.

5 33 − 99/3

6 Six equilateral triangles around a common vertex make this polygon.

7 2 puppies weigh 15 pounds. 6 puppies weigh N pounds.

9 6/15 + 3/15 = N/15

10 Metric volume measure equal to 1000 mL.

11 Compare: Mean of 2, 10 and 12 (more less same) mean of 8, 8 and 8.

12 A tree branch is 240 millimeters long. How many cm long is it?

13 28 is divisible by 2. Right or wrong?

15 Quadrilateral with 4 equal sides.

19 A regular triangle is more commonly called this.

21 7 flavors ice cream, 3 flavors of toppings. Choose one each, how many possible desserts?

23 Pattern: 3, 30, N, 250, 245, 2450, 2445.

25 The number 2 units to the left of 4 on the number line.

26 Missing digit: 30120.0525 ÷ 100.35 = 300.____5

27 The area of a right triangle with legs 6 and 2.

30 The mean of 5, 5 and 14.

31 A number with one pair of factors.

33 M = 7. Compare: 35 / M (more less same) 4.

34 7 is a factor of 77. Right or wrong?

38 66 ÷ N = 11

1. Which of the following describes a figure that has an area of 24 square centimeters?

○ A A rectangle with a length of 8 centimeters and a width of 4 centimeters

○ B A rectangle with a length of 3 centimeters and a width of 3 centimeters

○ C A rectangle with a length of 6 centimeters and a width of 4 centimeters

○ D A triangle that has three sides 8 centimeters long

2. What is the approximate measure of the obtuse angle in this triangle?

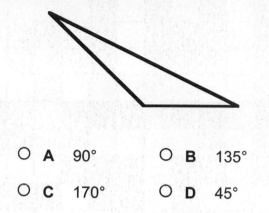

○ A 90°   ○ B 135°

○ C 170°   ○ D 45°

3. The rectangle below has an area of 36 square units and a perimeter of 36 units.

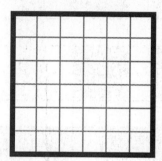

On the grid below, draw a rectangle that has the same area, but a different perimeter, from the rectangle above.

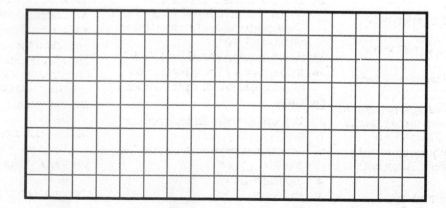

What is the perimeter, in units, of the new rectangle? _____

"Never mistake motion for action." — Ernest Hemingway, Author

/40

ACROSS

1 22/3 = 7 & N/3

2 27 ÷ [], if [] = 9.

3 3 cakes served 35 people. Next week 70 people, about how many cakes?

4 Figure A is congruent to figure B. Compare: area figure A (more less same) area figure B.

7 90/100 – 80/100 = N/100

9 Estimate 50/7 – 37/6 to the nearest unit.

10 A whole number and a fraction together make a ____ number.

11 The Calamarian grotnik coin is 4 mm thick. How high is a stack of 15 grotniks, in centimeters?

13 The lines on notebook paper are an example of ____ lines.

15 Word meaning that something will definitely happen.

17 Triangle: 15 area, height 5, base ____ .

18 An equilateral rectangle.

19 Start with 151. Do this 75 times: + 12, – 14.

21 The area of a right triangle with legs 6 and 8.

24 14/3 (more less same) 4.

25 The number 2 units to the left of 4 on the number line.

28 A number which is divisible by 2.

29 How many possible dinners if you choose 1 each of: 4 entrees, 2 vegetables?

31 5.80 + 7.20

33 A polygon is translated so that a vertex goes from (2,2) to (1,4). Another vertex goes from (8,6) to (N,8).

34 The area of an equilateral triangle with one side = 4 is 16. Right or wrong?

DOWN

1 Number of thousandths in 0.101

2 Area of rectangle = 120 sq. cm. L = 10 cm, W = ____ cm.

3 Compare: Mean of 7, 7, 7, 4 (more less same) mean of 10, 1, 5, and 9.

4 5.125 + 7/8

5 A number with more than one pair of factors.

6 N/10 dollar = 40 cents.

8 Greatest common factor of 15 and 25.

12 Prime factorization of 50 is $2 \times N \times 5$.

14 2 cm (more less same) 1 inch.

16 The mean of 10, 10 and 40.

20 Adding the same number over and over will generate these.

22 Missing digit: 205.604 ÷ 9.8 = 20.9____

23 6 thirds = N halves.

25 Pattern Machine. Input: 2, 6, 4, 5. Output: 8, 24, 16, N.

26 1 liter of water weighs this many kilograms.

27 0.142856 is approximately 1/N.

28 Rule: Divide by 2 and add 2. Pattern: 60, 32, 18, N.

30 23 is composite. Right or wrong?

32 R = 9. Compare: 9 + R (more less same) 81.

Parent/Gaurdian signature:

For puzzle time, return on:

1. Mallory did a survey of her classmates to see how many movies they watched during the summer. The data she collected is summarized here.

Students	Number of Movies Rented in Summer
Chloe	𝍤𝍤 𝍤𝍤 ||
Tyson	𝍤𝍤
Miguel	𝍤𝍤 𝍤𝍤𝍤𝍤 𝍤𝍤
Jayda	𝍤𝍤 𝍤𝍤	

What is the mean number of movies rented by these students?

○ **A** 5   ○ **B** 12

○ **C** 22   ○ **D** 40

2. Look at the diagram of the rectangle below.

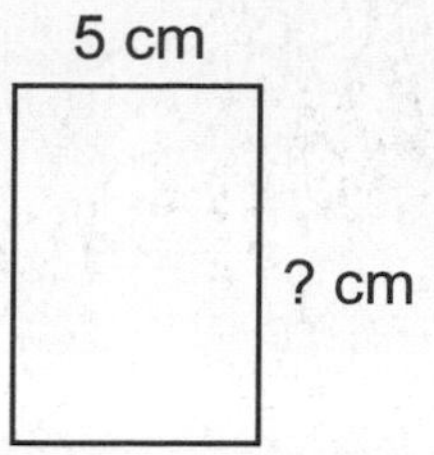

5 cm

? cm

The perimeter of the rectangle is 35 centimeters.

What is the missing measurement, in centimeters, of the rectangle?

○ **A** 35 cm   ○ **B** 15 cm

○ **C** 12.5 cm   ○ **D** 50 cm

3. Jose earns money by doing chores for his grandma. He is paid $4 for dusting, $3 for vacuuming, and $8 for shoveling the walk. Last week he shoveled the walk every morning before school and vacuumed twice, then he went to the store and bought a new book for $6.50.
How much money did Jose have left? Show your work in the space provided below.

"Whenever I don't have the answer to something, I find someone who does." — Walt Disney, Cartoonist

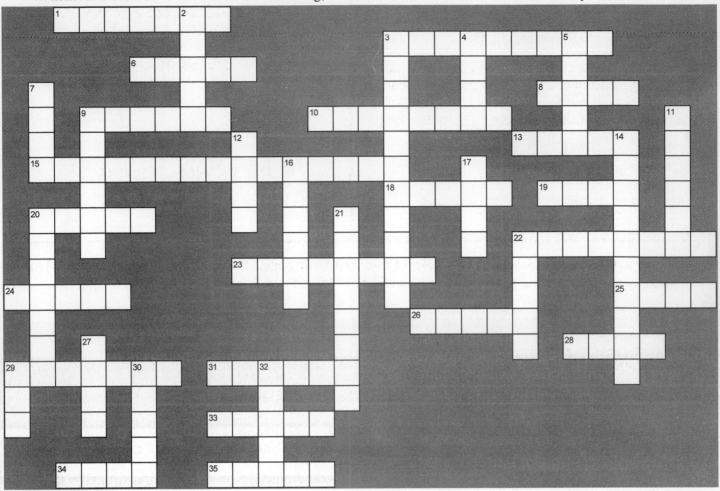

ACROSS

1 Area of rectangle = 120 sq. cm. L = 8 cm, W = ___ cm.

3 Start with 12. Do this 10 times: + 8, − 7.

6 2 is a factor of 76. Right or wrong?

8 A = 3. Compare: A + 10 (more less same) 12.

9 Least common multiple of 6 and 10.

10 The area of a right triangle with legs 7 and 4.

13 Pattern: 8, 5, 9, 6, 10, 7, 11, N.

15 If your brother is 1.6 meters tall, how many centimeters tall is that?

18 14/18 = N/9

19 3D shape that will hold your ice cream.

20 Eighths in 0.875

22 Secret Rule: {1, 2, 3, 4} matches {7, N, 21, 28}.

23 If you walk next to a friend and stay the distance apart, your paths are ___ .

24 0.55 + 2.48 + 6.05 is approximately 9. Right or wrong?

25 12/15 − 8/15 = N/15

26 A rectangle is cut along the diagonal. The two triangles are congruent. Right or wrong?

28 The number 0.5 units to the left of 4.5 on the number line.

29 A number like 1st, 2nd, 3rd.

31 The mean of 11, 12 and 13.

33 64 ÷ N = 8

34 25 = 5 × N

35 Basic unit of metric length, equal to 100 cm.

DOWN

2 A polygon is translated so that a vertex goes from (2,2) to (1,4). Another vertex goes from (8,6) to (7,N).

3 7 & 2/5 = N/5.

4 Missing digit: 7.80 × 8.07 = 62.___46

5 6 is a factor of 14. Right or wrong?

7 0.040 = 4 hundredths + N thousandths.

9 1200 cm = ___ meters.

11 Triangle: 72 area, base 12, height ___ .

12 3/6 (more less same) 3/4.

14 I am a multiple of 6 and 8. I am less than 25.

16 Multiply a whole number by itself and you'll get a ___ number.

17 Compare: Area of triangle with B = 9 and H = 12 (more less same) area of rectangle with L = 5 and W = 11.

20 Same shape, but not necessarily same size.

21 AA batteries are approximately this shape.

22 Heads comes up on a coin flip about N times out of 100.

27 Kurt's scores: 88, 90, 92. Kirk's scores: 88, 92, 94. Who has the greatest mean?

29 2 tenths = N fifths.

30 At 7:45 a clock's hands form which angle: acute, right, or obtuse?

32 @ = 64, ★ = 8. What is @ ÷ ★?

1. Each letter in the word

B R I L L I A N T

is written on a separate piece of paper and put into a bag. One of the pieces of paper is selected from the bag at random. What is the probability that the piece of paper selected will be the letter *l*?

   ○ **A**   1/9   ○ **B**   2/9

   ○ **C**   6/9   ○ **D**   7/9

2. On Thursday, a train left Seattle at 6:11 A.M. and arrived in San Francisco at 9:51 P.M. How long did the trip take?

   ○ **A**   16 hours, 30 minutes

   ○ **B**   3 hours, 30 minutes

   ○ **C**   3 hours, 50 minutes

   ○ **D**   15 hours, 40 minutes

3, The owners of Main Street Movies need to reorder their popcorn for their concession stand. The table below shows the popcorn sales at Main Street Movies last Friday.

Popcorn	Number Sold
Small	69
Medium	51
Large	42
Jumbo	14
Special	83

Small: 1 cup popcorn
Medium: 2 cups popcorn
Large: 3 cups popcorn
Jumbo: 5 cups popcorn
Special: 1 small popcorn & 1 small drink

Use the chart and the information given above to determine how many cups of popcorn are used each day. Explain your work using words, numbers, or pictures.

"Things turn out best for the people who make the best of the way things turn out." — Art Linkletter, Personality

ACROSS

2 0.1667 is approximately 1/N.

3 Compare: 55 + 5.10 (more less same) 60.

6 48 = 2 × 2 × 2 × 2 × N

10 Secret Rule: {2, 6, 5, 10} matches {4, 12, 10, N}.

12 75 is divisible by 2. Right or wrong?

14 One thousand grams equals N kilograms.

17 3/2 = N/8

19 Find the composite: 71, 73, 81, 79.

20 27 ÷ N = 3

21 Chance of rolling a one on a six-sided die = 1/N.

22 Triangle: 1 area, base 2, height ___ .

25 The area of an equilateral triangle with one side = 6 is 12. Right or wrong?

28 Number of ways to choose 1 of 5 colors and 1 of 5 shapes.

31 A translation is also known as a ___ .

32 Box of 7 costs $2.80. Unit price = N¢.

33 A textbook is 25 mm thick. How many meters tall is a stack of 120 textbooks?

34 Rule: Add 6 and divide by 2. Pattern: 22, 14, 10, N.

35 Compare: Area of triangle with B = 9 and H = 12 (more less same) area of rectangle with L = 2 and W = 25.

36 Start with 20. Do this 20 times: + 10, − 9.

37 A quadrilateral can have 5 sides. Right or wrong?

DOWN

1 The number 0.5 units to the right of 4.5 on the number line.

4 It is possible to put two triangles together to make a square. Right or wrong?

5 Information that helps you understand a graph.

6 16.01 + 2.005 + 1.988 is approximately what integer?

7 A polygon is translated so that a vertex goes from (3,6) to (1,4). Another vertex goes from (6,7) to (4,N).

8 1 + 2 = 3. The 1 and 2 in that number sentence are called what?

9 The system we use where digits are worth different amounts depending on where they are. (Two words.)

10 Value of "3" in 5.023 = 3 ___ .

11 The U.S. has been officially metric since 1894 . True or false?

13 Missing digit: 20.41 ÷ 15.7 = ___.3

15 Cats: 15, 16, 6 pounds. Dogs: 15, 15, 8 pounds. Highest mean?

16 The leftover portion when dividing.

18 8 is a factor of 14. Right or wrong?

23 Pattern 5, 10, 9, 14, 13, 18, 17, N.

24 2/5 dollars = N cents.

26 A 126° angle is ___ .

27 The area of a right triangle with legs 8 and 4.

29 # = 25 and $ = 5. Find # ÷ $.

30 9/10 (more less same) 3/2.

32 2 thirds = N sixths.

1. Megan bought 6 roses priced at $2.25 each. She used a coupon worth $1.50 off the total cost. Which number sentence can be used to find how much money Megan needed in order to buy the roses?

- ○ **A** $(6 \times 1.50) - 2.25 = 6.75$
- ○ **B** $(6 + 2.25) + 1.50 = 8.75$
- ○ **C** $(6 - 2.25) + 1.50 = 5.25$
- ○ **D** $(6 \times 2.25) - 1.50 = 12.00$

2. Look at this grid:

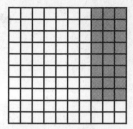

What part of this grid is shaded?

- ○ **A** 24%
- ○ **B** 30%
- ○ **C** 3 %
- ○ **D** 8%

3. Look at the number pattern below.

358, 371, 384, 397, _____, _____

What are the next two numbers in the number pattern? Explain your work using words, numbers, or pictures.

ACROSS

5 4/25 = N/75

7 The denominator tells the ____ of each fraction part.

10 Area of square = 36. Side of square = N.

11 Find the prime: 5, 25, 15, 1.

12 11000 g = N kg

14 Compare: 10.8 – .8 (more less same) 11.

15 B = 50. Compare: 100 – B (more less same) 50.

19 5 & N/3 = 25/3

23 A polygon is translated so that a vertex goes from (3,6) to (1,4). Another vertex goes from (6,7) to (N,5).

24 Changing a number to a nearby multiple of 10 or 100.

25 Least common multiple of 20 and 15.

29 The mean of 2, 10, and 12.

30 Mathematical name for a perfect ball.

31 6 different shirts, 2 different pants. Number of outfits?

32 A polygon can have 7 equal sides. Right or wrong?

33 The perimeter of an equilateral triangle with one side = 8 is 16. Right or wrong?

34 Pattern Machine. Input: 12, 7, 0, 10. Output: 13, N, 1, 11.

35 14/15 – 7/15 = N/15

DOWN

1 The two lower-case l's in "parallel" are examples of ____ lines.

2 Rule: Multiply by 8 and subtract 7. Pattern: 1, 1, N, 1.

3 The number of cubic units which fill a space.

4 N ninths = 2.

5 3.25 – 2/8

6 Fractions which have the same value are ____ .

8 The line segments making up a polygon are called ____ .

9 $0.75 = N/8 dollar.

10 Compare: Area of triangle with B = 5 and H = 10 (more less same) area of triangle with B = 2 and H = 25.

13 2 is a factor of 67. Right or wrong?

16 Triangle: 1 area, base 1, height ____ .

17 A spinner is split into 5 equal regions numbered 1-5. Chance of spinning even number = N/5.

18 Prime factorization of 65 is 5 × N.

19 29.4 + 3/5

20 A 92° angle is ____ .

21 If & = 9, what is 45 ÷ & ?

22 Pattern: 14, 28, 18, 36, 26, 52, N.

23 N ÷ 2 = 7

24 A square is cut along the diagonal. The two triangles are isosceles. Right or wrong?

26 Estimate 41/8 + 87/11 to the nearest unit.

27 0.020 = N/1000

28 32 is a factor of 60. Right or wrong?

1. Eric made a chart of how he spent his time after school for one week.

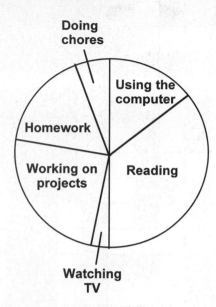

Approximately how much of Eric's after school time was spent on projects?

- **A** 1/2
- **B** 3/5
- **C** 1/4
- **D** 1/10

2. The Hometown Press surveyed its readers to determine how much time each age group spent reading its newspaper each day. Below is a chart of the survey results.

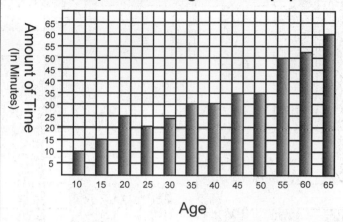

- **A** The amount of time readers spend reading the newspaper goes down with age.
- **B** Overall, the older a reader is, the more time they spend reading the newspaper.
- **C** Older readers always spend more time reading the newspaper than younger readers.
- **D** Reading the newspaper makes readers smarter.

3. Yulisa and her family built 63 birdhouses. They plan to give them to the 9 local elementary schools, giving each of them an equal number of birdhouses. In the space provided below, write a number sentence that can be used to find how many birdhouses each school will receive.

"A book is like a garden carried in the pocket." — Chinese Proverb

ACROSS

2 The longest measure across a circle.

5 N/9 = 1 & 4/9.

10 $0.25 = 2/N dollar.

11 The perimeter of an equilateral triangle with one side = 8 is 24. Right or wrong?

13 Number of 30° angles that will fit neatly around a point.

16 A 175° angle is ____ .

18 A spinner is split into 10 equal regions numbered 1-10. Chance of spinning a number divisible by 3 = N/10.

19 Compare: 4.62 + 5.22 (more less same) 10.

20 Rule: Subtract 2 and double. Pattern: 6, 8, 12, N.

22 40 ÷ N = 4

24 The number 0.5 units to the right of 11.5 on the number line.

26 The result of a multiplication operation.

27 3/2 (more less same) 6/4.

28 Compare: Area of triangle with B = 5 and H = 10 (more less same) area of triangle with B = 7 and H = 8.

30 Compare: Mean of 0, 1 and 20 (more less same) mean of 7, 7 and 6.

31 Missing digit: 2064.15 ÷ 2.75 = 750.____

32 98.6 + 2/5

33 5280 feet.

34 Feet in a yard.

35 The mean of 5, 5 and 8.

DOWN

1 Find the composite: 85, 5, 83, 31.

3 The first place after a decimal point tells how many of these.

4 44 is divisible by 2. Right or wrong?

6 9 is a factor of 90. Right or wrong?

7 The number of endpoints of a line.

8 A rhombus with right angles.

9 2 dogs weigh 35 pounds. 4 dogs weigh N pounds.

11 This angle is greater than an acute angle but less than an obtuse.

12 A box is 1/5 of a meter long. How many millimeters long is it?

14 Greatest common factor of 16 and 24.

15 14/15 + 7/15 = N/15

17 5 flavors of ice cream, 5 flavors of toppings. Choose one each, how many possible desserts?

20 Pattern: 7, 14, 13, 26, N, 50, 49.

21 Half the measure of a right angle, in degrees.

23 Area of square = 16. Side of square = N.

24 The area of a right triangle with legs 9 and 8.

25 100 − 198/2

27 Start with 170. Do this 100 times: + 4, − 5.

29 5/10 = 8/N

31 M = 12. Compare: 36 / M (more less same) 3.

1. There are two red, four purple, and two orange gumballs in a bag. Without looking in the bag, what are the chances of picking a purple gumball out of the bag?

○ **A** 10%

○ **B** 25%

○ **C** 50%

○ **D** 87.5%

2. All the customers in the mall eating at Kent's Burgers bought two hamburgers on Thursday. Brittany bought one hamburger. Based on this information, which **must be true**?

○ **A** If Brittany brought one hamburger, then she was not at the mall on Thursday.

○ **B** If Brittany brought one hamburger, then she did not eat at Kent's Burgers.

○ **C** If Brittany brought one hamburger, then she ate at Kent's Burgers.

○ **D** If Brittany brought one hamburger, then she ate at Tokyo House.

3. The perimeter of **parallelogram ABCD** below is 50 meters.

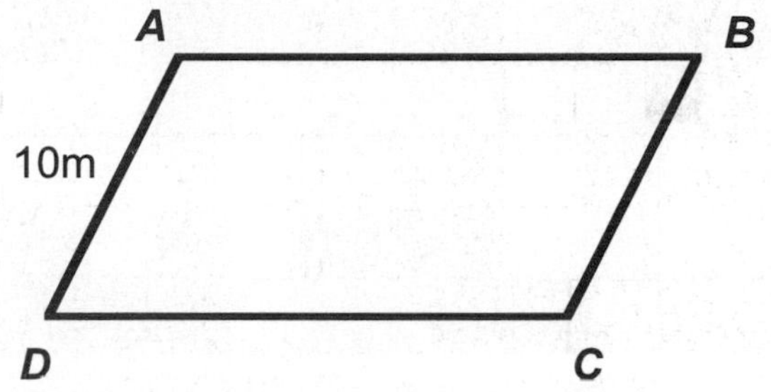

What is the length of side *AB*? _____

Explain your answer using words, pictures, or numbers.

89

"We cannot become what we need to be by remaining what we are." — Max de Pree, Author

ACROSS

2 The mean of 20, 20 and 50.

4 Compare: Mean of 5, 5, 3, 7 (more less same) mean of 0, 4, 10, and 6.

6 5 cakes served 100 people. Next week 300 people, about how many cakes?

12 Number of thousandths in 0.092

15 Rule: Divide by 2 and add 2. Pattern: 76, 40, 22, N.

16 A triangle can have three 30° angles. Right or wrong?

17 seven-eighths + 3.125

20 How many possible dinners if you choose 1 each of: 2 entrees, 2 vegetables?

22 Pattern Machine. Input: 3, 4, 5, 6. Output: 6, 8, 10, N.

23 (2,3) is translated 1 to the right. New position is (N,3).

24 Start with 78. Do this 75 times: + 2, − 3.

26 A ____ diagram has loops to show how things are related.

27 Missing digit: 50.36 × 50.63 = 2549.____268

28 Lines which meet at 90°.

30 A portion of a circle.

34 If two things have the same chance of happening, they are ____. (Two words.)

35 Greatest common factor of 8 and 6.

37 Number of mm in two meters.

38 0.875 = N/8

DOWN

1 The number 2.5 units to the left of 15.5 on the number line.

3 N/5 dollar = 60 cents.

5 1/1000 of a liter.

6 75 = 3 × 5 × N

7 Triangle: 25 area, base 1, height ____ .

8 17/2 = 8 & N/2.

9 20 tenths = N halves.

10 2.95 + 5.05

11 A number > 1 whose only divisors are 1 and itself.

13 If the elevation of Bellingham is 0.3 km, how many meters above sea level is Bellingham?

14 Estimate 41/5 − 29/7 to the nearest unit.

18 9/2 (more less same) 6.

19 Area of square = 9. Side of square = N.

21 The order in which you do calculations is the order of ____ .

25 90 ÷ [], if [] = 3.

29 57 is composite. Right or wrong?

31 The perimeter of an equilateral triangle with one side = 5 is 15. Right or wrong?

32 R = 5. Compare: 6+R (more less same) 30.

33 The area of a right triangle with legs 10 and 1.

35 Number of diagonals of a quadrilateral.

36 15/100 − 5/100 = N/100

1. Rewrite this expression:

    $6^4 =$

    ○ **A** $6 \times 6 \times 6 \times 6$

    ○ **B** $4 \times 4 \times 4 \times 4 \times 4 \times 4$

    ○ **C** $6 + 6 + 6 + 6$

    ○ **D** $4 + 4 + 4 + 4 + 4 + 4$

2. Davis has 82 trading cards. Aiden has 12 less than Davis. The number of cards owned by Davis, Aiden, and Clara adds up to 214. Which equation can be used to determine how many cards Clara owns?

    ○ **A** $82 + (82 - 12) + C = 214$

    ○ **B** $214 + (82 - 12) + 82 = C$

    ○ **C** $82 + (82 - 12) = 214 + C$

    ○ **D** $214 + C = 214 + 9$

3. Tanya's mom is creating a budget for her family by saving receipts from their purchases for a month. After three weeks, her budget chart showed the results below.

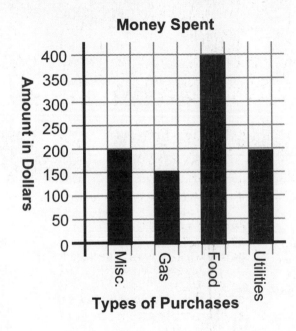

Money Spent

After the fourth week, Tanya's mom added in the final week's receipts. She spent an additional $37 on food and $30 on gas.

How much money, total, did Tanya's mom spend during the month? _____

Explain your answer.

_____

_____

_____

"What the heart knows today the head will understand tomorrow." — James Stephens, Author

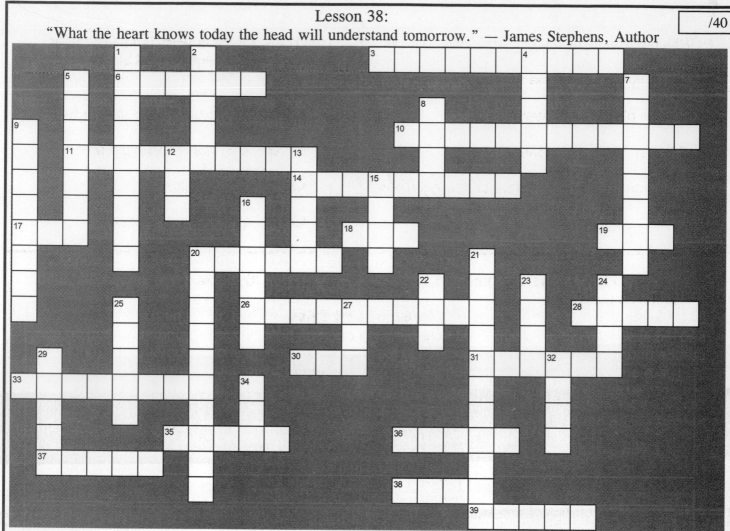

ACROSS

3 1/10 of a centimeter.

6 The measure from the center of a circle to its edge.

10 A satellite is roughly 800,000 meters above the earth. How many kilometers up is that?

11 Least common multiple of 8 and 12.

14 Triangle with two equal sides.

17 9.325 + five-eighths.

18 Amy's scores: 0, 6, 10. Ann's scores: 4, 5, 6. Who has the greatest mean?

19 The area of a right triangle with legs 10 and 2.

20 The mean of 19, 20 and 21.

26 Heads comes up on a coin flip about N times out of 50.

28 6 is a factor of 30. Right or wrong?

30 @ = 10, ★ = 5. What is @ ÷ ★ ?

31 Area of square = 144. Side of square = N.

33 The number 3.5 units to the right of 15.5 on the number line.

35 1 is a prime number. Right or wrong?

36 An equilateral triangle can be folded in half to make a right triangle. Right or wrong?

37 11/20 − 8/20 = N/20

38 Missing digit: 200.05 × 100.50 = 2010____.02____

39 56 ÷ N = 7

DOWN

1 Quadrilateral with one pair of parallel sides.

2 Total number of toes on quintuplets.

4 Secret Rule: {1, 2, 3, 4} matches {N, 16, 24, 32}.

5 I am a multiple of 3 and 15. I am less than 20.

7 If you walk next to a friend and stay the distance apart, your paths are ____ .

8 0.055 = 5 hundredths + N thousandths.

9 Start with 3. Do this 10 times: + 10, − 9.

12 6 ninths = N thirds.

13 2 is a factor of 22. Right or wrong?

15 Compare: Area of triangle with B = 2 and H = 14 (more less same) area of triangle with B = 7 and H = 4.

16 2 thirds = N thirtieths.

20 One-fifth of a meter is N mm.

21 11 & 1/2 = N/2

22 Pattern: 20, 15, 17, 12, 14, 9, 11, N.

23 1/2 (more less same) 1/4 .

24 Prime factorization of 70 is 2 × N × 7.

25 A 8° angle is ____ .

27 (2,2) is translated 1 to the right. New position is (3,N).

29 10.02 + 20.50 + 5.52 is approximately 36. Right or wrong?

32 A = 8. Compare: A + 18 (more less same) 28.

34 Rectangle: 6 area, width 2, perimeter N.

Parent/Gaurdian signature:

For puzzle time, return on:

1. Which of the following figures is **not** possible.

○ **A** A right scalene triangle.

○ **B** An obtuse equilateral triangle

○ **C** A rhombus with one right angle.

○ **D** A quadrilateral with four congruent sides

2. Heather wants to construct a rectangular prism from paper shapes. What shapes will she need?

○ **A** 2 triangles and 3 rectangles

○ **B** 4 triangles and a square

○ **C** 6 rectangles

○ **D** 2 circles and 3 squares

3. The chart below shows the total number of snow shovels sold at a local hardware store during select months last year.

Snow Shovel Sales During Select Months

Month	Shovels Sold
July	0
September	15
November	57
January	134
March	25

During which month was the greatest number of snow shovels sold? _____

Give two possible reasons that would explain why the greatest number of shovels were sold during the month you named?

_____

_____

_____

_____

_____

_____

93

"People don't really care how much you know until they know how much you care." — Mike McKnight, Musician

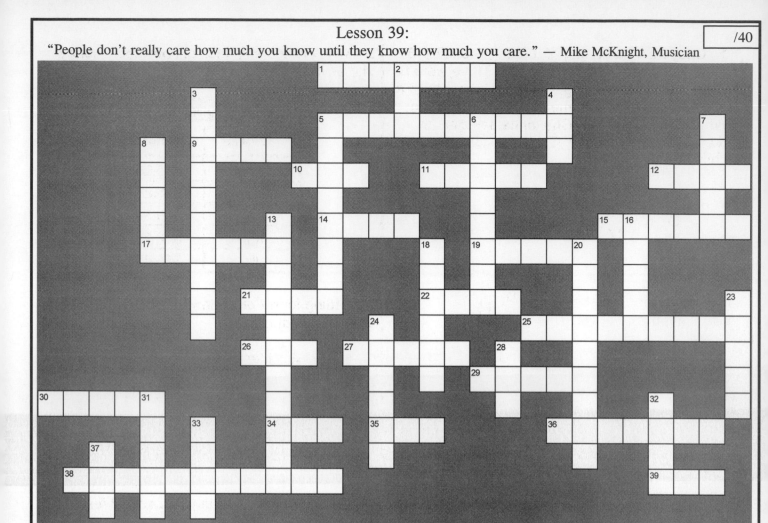

ACROSS

1 Find the composite: 7, 11, 13, 15.

5 5/20 dollars = N cents.

9 4/5 (more less same) 2/1.

10 Missing digit: 4046.12 ÷ 50.2 = 80.___

11 A 68° angle is ___ .

12 Cats: 10, 20, 20 pounds. Dogs: 25, 15, 12 pounds. Highest mean?

14 2.25 × 4

15 11.004 + 5.99 + 3.002 is approximately what integer?

17 The closest integer to the right of 11.7 on the number line.

19 4 thirds = N sixths.

21 Compare: 12.8 + 13.2 (more less same) 25.

22 36 ÷ N = 4

25 Type of graph using line segments.

26 (4,6) is translated 2 to the left. New position is (2,N).

27 The area of a rectangle is 20, and the length is 4. The width of the rectangle is 5. Right or wrong?

29 60,000 millimeters equals N meters.

30 A square can be cut to make a triangle and a pentagon. Right or wrong?

34 Start with 50. Do this 20 times: + 5, – 7.

35 Zander had 8 apples. He gave away all but 2. How many remain?

36 The area of a right triangle with legs 10 and 3.

38 You and your friend Pat live 0.5 km away. How many meters away does Pat live?

39 # = 18 and $ = 3. Find # ÷ $.

DOWN

2 Number of ways to choose 1 of 5 colors and 1 of 2 shapes.

3 1/1000 of a meter.

4 Rule: Add 6 and divide by 2. Pattern: 38, 22, 14, N.

5 A polygon with the least number of sides possible.

6 Rectangle: 12 area, width 3, perimeter N.

7 8 is a factor of 24. Right or wrong?

8 28/32 = 7/N

13 Tells how big the parts are in a fraction.

16 53 is divisible by 2. Right or wrong?

18 Value of "9" in 8.905 = 9 ___ .

20 Pattern 4, 8, 10, 14, 16, 20, 22, N.

23 33 = N × 11

24 Box of 3 costs $2.70. Unit price = N¢.

28 Chance of rolling an odd or an even number on a six-sided die = N/6.

31 Number of equal sides in an equilateral triangle.

32 Compare: Area of triangle with B = 8 and H = 3 (more less same) area of triangle with B = 7 and H = 4.

33 Maximum number of right angles in a quadrilateral.

37 Secret Rule: {3, 7, 6, 10} matches {N, 14, 12, 20}.

1. Cheyenne had a bag of 3 orange candies, 6 green candies, and 8 red candies. There were no other candies in the bag. Cheyenne reached in a chose one candy from the bag, without looking. What is the probability Cheyenne selected an orange or a red candy? Circle the correct answer.

○ **A** $\dfrac{3}{17}$ ○ **B** $\dfrac{8}{17}$

○ **C** $\dfrac{11}{17}$ ○ **D** $\dfrac{6}{17}$

2. Mindy is keeping track of how much money she saves.

Monthly Savings	
Month	Amount
March	$15.25
April	$16.23
May	$16.39
June	$16.93
July	$15.45

According to this table, in which month did Mindy save the least money?

○ **A** March   ○ **B** April

○ **C** June   ○ **D** July

3. Adam is ordering gifts for his family for the holidays from the book store. He has saved $72 to spend on the items in the chart below.

Items to Purchase	
Items	Price (in dollars)
Book on CD	23.99
Calendar	8.75
Picture Book	12.99
Cookbook	26.47
New Release	16.99
Bookmark	2.50
Gift Card	10.00

Create 2 possible lists of items Adam could buy that cost at least $65, but not more than $72.

List 1

_____

_____

_____

_____

_____

List 2

_____

_____

_____

_____

_____

Explain your work using words, numbers, or pictures.

ACROSS

2 Compare: Area of triangle with B = 6 and H = 5 (more less same) area of triangle with B = 7 and H = 4.

4 Rectangle: 9 area, width 3, perimeter N.

5 8 = 2 × 2 × N

6 10 different shirts, 3 different pants. Number of outfits?

8 5 & N/8 = 46/8.

9 If you cut a quadrilateral along the diagonal, you get two of these.

12 4/6 − 2/6 = N/6

16 If & = 8, what is 32 ÷ & ?

18 The mean of 3, 4, and 14.

21 1 half = N tenths.

22 N ÷ 7 = 3

24 Left arm straight up, right arm straight out. Arms form what angle?

25 Fractions that are the same, like 1/2, and 2/4, are called this.

26 A line segment connecting any two points on a circle.

27 A spinner is split into 5 equal regions numbered 1-5. Chance of spinning a number greater than 2 = N/5.

28 A regular hexagon can be cut to make 6 equilateral triangles. Right or wrong?

30 The average angle measure of a parallelogram.

32 Pattern Machine. Input: 2, 0, 7, 11. Output: 4, 0, 14, N.

33 The area of a rectangle is 2, and the length is 1. The width of the rectangle is 1. Right or wrong?

DOWN

1 Compare: 22 − 2.2 (more less same) 20.

2 B = 19. Compare: 40 − B (more less same) 20.

3 4000 millimeters equals N meters.

4 Another name for "rotation".

6 9/15 = N/45

7 0.011 = N/1000

9 $0.90 = 9/N dollar.

10 Triangle with no equal sides.

11 The two lower-case l's in "parallel" are examples of ____ lines.

12 0.375 = N/8

13 Find the prime: 7, 27, 1, 72.

14 Pattern 100, 50, 60, 30, 40, N, 30.

15 Denominators which are the same are ____ denominators.

17 Estimate 52/10 + 89/10 to the nearest unit.

18 Least common multiple of 12 and 15.

19 Minimum number of angles in a polygon.

20 17 is a factor of 34. Right or wrong?

21 Rule: Multiply by 5 and subtract 6. Pattern: 2, 4, N, 64.

23 2 is a factor of 51. Right or wrong?

29 Area of square = 4. Side of square = N.

31 (3,11) is translated 2 up and 1 left. New position is (N,13).

1. Which rectangle has an area of 36 square units and a perimeter of 40 units?

○ A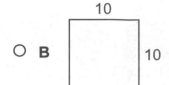
12

3

○ B
10

10

○ C
6

6

○ D
18

2

2. Which equation shows the relationship between all of the values in the table below?

x	y
0	0
18	6
27	9
57	19

○ A $y = \dfrac{x}{3}$ ○ B $x = y + 12$

○ C $y = 4x$ ○ D $x = 3 - y$

3. Consider the following pattern of figures.

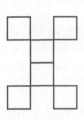   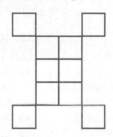   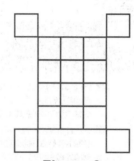   _____

Figure 1   **Figure 2**   **Figure 3**   **Figure 4**

Sketch a picture of the next figure in the space provided.

How many unit squares are there in Figure 4?   _____

How many unit squares would be in the 10th figure?   _____

Explain your answer in the space below:

_____

_____

_____

_____

"Not knowing when the dawn will come, I open every doo

Handwritten note (top right):
Mistake
#23A
Should be - (2)^2 ?
answer should be
right

ACROSS

6 10000 = 100 squared. Right or wrong?

7 2 to the power of –4.

8 Right or wrong? TOT reflected across y-axis still reads TOT.

10 0.151 (more less same) one eighth.

14 5(2 + 8) = 2(5 + 8). Right or wrong?

15 12N – 29 = 7N – 4

17 Rectangular prism has surface area 11. If linear dimensions are doubled, new surface area is ____ .

21 Newspaper costs 50 cents; first 2 are free. Cost for 30 days = $N.

22 If R – 58 ? 8 then R ? ____ .

23 Right or wrong? (-2) ^ 2 ? 0.4 x -10

25 120 miles per two hours= ____ miles per quarter hour.

26 Missing digit: 7 ^ 5 = 16____07.

27 4/500 kilogram = N grams.

28 Number of wonders of ancient world.

29 Cylinder: Radius = N, height = 14, volume = 1134 x pi.

30 Multiplicative inverse of 0.2 is 0.5. Right or wrong?

32 5 inch wide by 6.5 inch long photo is enlarged to make photo N inches wide by 13 inches long.

35 Diagram using overlapping circles to represent relationships between sets is a ____ diagram.

37 Cross-section of prism could be circle. Right or wrong?

38 Right or wrong? Quadrilateral w/three vertices at (5,2), (5,-3), and (7,1) could be a rhombus.

40 Chance of drawing red nine from deck of cards: N in 52.

41 Linear relationship: (2,3.75), (3,5.5), (4,7.25), (5,N).

42 Ten-sided polygon.

43 In class of five, four scores are 96%, 82%, 83% and 61%,. The highest possible median score is ____%.

DOWN

1 Distance between points (1,1) and (13,N) is 13. (N is positive.)

2 Equilateral parallelogram.

3 2/3 ÷ 2/3 (more less same) 2/3 x 2/3.

4 70+ 56Y = 7(____ + 8Y)

5 Right triangle has sides 60 and 80, hypotenuse N.

9 How many squares in {1600, 25000, 360, 14400} ?

11 Rectangular arrangement of quantities in rows and columns, as in a matrix.

12 On roulette wheel, 18 of 38 numbers are red. Chance of wheel spinning red two times in a row is N/361.

13 Snowflake is based on this polygon.

16 10 gallon tank holds 24 guppies. 15 gallon tank holds 36. Gallons needed for 120 guppies?

18 Cube root of 9261.

19 Length of fabric 3 yards long has 5 frogs printed on it. There are about N frogs (closest integer) on 5 yards of fabric.

20 Jeans cost $12 in 1976, $42 in 1996. Average rate of change is ____ dollars/decade.

22 Price of CD decreased 15% to $13.60. Original price: $N.

24 Area of right triangle w/legs 25 and 8.

28 4/10 squared (more less same) 4/25.

31 Writing 0.4397623 as 0.44 is an example of this.

33 Triangle w/sides {28,18,24} is similar to a triangle w/sides {70, 45, N}.

34 60 square tiles cover 15 sq. ft. Side length of one tile: 1/N ft.

36 What is the ones' digit of 3^10?

39 Roll a die and get a three. Right or wrong? Next roll is more likely to be even than odd.

1. Andre earned $21.00 on Monday, $8.00 on Tuesday, and then, spent $5 on Wednesday. Which number sentence shows how much money Andre had left?

- A (21 + 8) + 5 = n
- B (21 × 8) – 5 = n
- C (21 + 8) – 5 = n
- D 21 – (8 – 5) = n

2. What is the area of this figure?

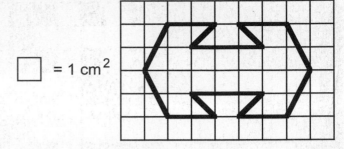

☐ = 1 cm^2

- A 12 cm^2
- B 17.5 cm^2
- C 18.5 cm^2
- D 20 cm^2

3. Maddie collects horses with exchangeable saddles. Every month she saves enough to purchase one more horse for her collection. How many months will it take for her to purchase all of the different possible combinations of horses and saddles?

Hobby Horses	
Types of Horses	Saddle Colors
Bay	Brown
Pinto	Black
Sorrel	Polka-dot
Palomino	Red
Roan	Blue

Explain your work using words, numbers, or pictures.

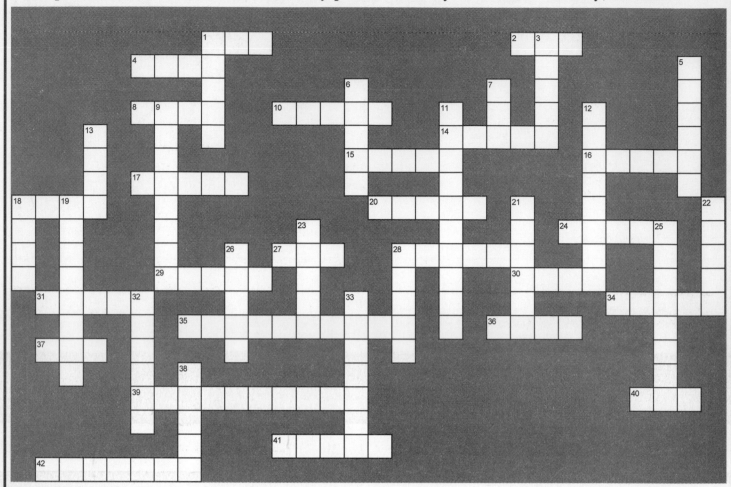

ACROSS

1 15 fifths = N halves.

2 If 6 is 1.5 inches from 4 on a number line, what number is 1.5 inches to the left of 4?

4 22/6 (more less same) 3.

8 Number of thousandths in 0.005

10 Volume is measured in ___ units.

14 A triangle can have an obtuse angle and a right angle. Right or wrong?

15 What is the opposite of -3?

16 Right or wrong? On a number line, 17 is to the left of 19.

17 Right or wrong? 13.22 – 1/4 is approximately 12.

18 3 ÷ 5 = 3/N

20 1/2 = N%

24 Find the integer: 1/2, 8, 10.2

27 36 ÷ [], if [] = 6.

28 On a number line, start at 8, go 3 left, 7 right. Where are you?

29 The perimeter of a rectangle is 6, and the length is 1. The width of the rectangle is 2. Right or wrong?

30 3/7 (more less same) 4/7.

31 Right or wrong: 50% of 10 ≥ 0.5 × 10.

34 Jen worked 2.25 hours in the morning, and 3/4 hour in the afternoon. Total hours worked?

35 12.6 + 12.4

36 N, 5, 10, 15, 30, 35, 70, 75, 150.

37 A jar has greater volume than a can. Which will hold more water?

39 The mean of 10, 20, 30 and 40.

40 9/8 – seven-eights + 0.75

41 Right or wrong? Volume is measured in square units.

42 Bees like this shape.

DOWN

1 15/35 = 3/N

3 10 is a factor of 101. Right or wrong?

5 The angle sum of a rectangle, in degrees, is 330 + N.

6 Two lines intersect making a 120° angle. Other angle's measure?

7 (7,6) is translated down 2, left 5. New position is (N,4).

9 A fraction like 7/4, whose numerator is greater than its denominator.

11 5 tenths = 10 ___ .

12 Famous giant shapes in Egypt.

13 Compare: Area of 3 by 12 rectangle (more less same) area of 2 by 18 rectangle.

18 7 × N + 1 = 36

19 A horizontal and a ___ line are perpendicular.

21 How many possible dinners if you choose 1 each of: 2 entrees, 6 vegetables?

22 18/5 = 3 & N/5

23 A certain triangle has angles 30°, N°, and 90°.

25 3c + 7 when c = 2.

26 3 × 101 = 101 × N

28 1% of 300.

32 A probability of 3 out of 10 = N%.

33 Pattern Pairs: (5, 11) (20, 41) (100, 201) (7,N).

38 Rule: Divide by 5 and add 5. Pattern: 100, 25, 10, N.

1. What is 5/6 written as a percent?

    ○ **A** 5.6 %

    ○ **B** $83\frac{1}{3}$ %

    ○ **C** $60\frac{1}{2}$ %

    ○ **D** 89 %

2. Look at the circle below.

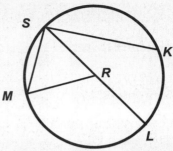

Which of the following line segments is the radius of the circle?

    ○ **A** $\overline{SL}$ ○ **B** $\overline{SK}$

    ○ **C** $\overline{SM}$ ○ **D** $\overline{RM}$

---

3. Elliot wants to install a fence around his ostrich farm as shown below.

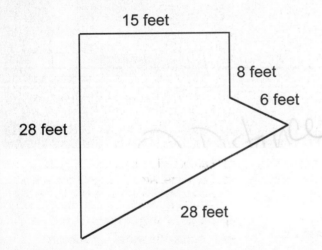

Price of Fencing	
Fencing Type	Price (per foot)
Chain Link	$15
Tall Wood	$13
Short Wood	$11
Plastic	$18

What is the least amount of money it will cost Elliot to build the fence? _____

Explain your answer in the space below.

"I had rather do and not promise than promise and not do." — Arthur Warwick, Author

ACROSS

4 A ____ decimal is a decimal that goes on and on like 0.3333333

5 Two lines that never meet are ____ .

6 Volume is measured in ____ units.

7 Right or wrong? 9.52 + five-halves is about 10.

11 Tool for measuring angles.

14 5/2 − 1/2

15 3/8 (more less same) 3/9.

16 Right or wrong? The ratio 4 to 7 can be written 4/7.

18 A right triangle's short leg is 4, and its long leg is 9. What's the area?

19 If 5 is 6 inches from 7 on a number line, what number is 3 inches to the left of 6?

20 Six boxes on two trucks is the same ratio as N boxes on 5 trucks.

21 Rectangle: 10 perimeter, width 4, area N.

23 44 ÷ N = 22

24 Number of diagonals in a hexagon.

26 Number of sides in a heptagon (or septagon).

28 R = 2. Compare: 98 + R (more less same) 100.

29 36 inches.

30 Start with 50. Do this 75 times: + 7, − 5.

32 252 ÷ 3 is not an integer. Right or wrong?

33 N ÷ 2 = 14 + 1

34 3/50 = N%

36 Add two terms to get the next. Pattern: 3, 4, 7, 11, 18, N.

38 43 + ____ = 2 × 25

40 2 × ____ − 10 = 20

41 1 × 2 × 3 × 4 × 5 × 6 × 7 × 8 × 9 × 0

DOWN

1 Two figures which are the same shape but not necessarily the same size are ____ .

2 The perimeter of a rectangle is 20, and the length is 4. The width of the rectangle is 5. Right or wrong?

3 The areas of the sides of a pyramid are 5, 3, 3, 3, and 3. What is its surface area?

7 50% of 10 > 10% of 50. Right or wrong?

8 0.4 = N/5

9 (4 + 25) + 15 = N + (25 + 15)

10 2.5 meters = N cm.

12 An apartment building is 3600 cm tall. How many meters tall is that?

13 In 0.187, the digit 8 is in the ____ place.

17 2 carrots per bunny plus 3 for me. 5 bunnies, how many carrots?

19 Which is an integer: 14÷3, 3/4, 5?

21 2/3 × 2/5 = N/15

22 Right or wrong? To find how much paint needed for a room, first find the surface area.

25 CARTON holds 2750, BUNDLE holds 2775. Which holds fewer?

27 Pattern Machine. Input: 3, 7, 9, 6. Output: 9, 21, 27, N.

31 5y − 5 when y = 5.

35 One angle of an equilateral triangle is this many degrees.

36 5/6 + 15/7 is approximately what integer?

37 The nth term of the pattern 3, 6, 9, 12, 15…is ____ × n.

1. Willie collected rainfall data for the following seven months and wants to find the range of the data.

Months	Centimeters of Rain
August	3.8
September	6.2
October	10.59
November	6.06
December	12.4
January	12.37
February	18.3

What is the difference between the wettest and the driest months in the table?

○ **A** 7.47 cm   ○ **B** 8.6 cm

○ **C** 4.62 cm   ○ **D** 6.3 . cm

2. Jake needs to enclose his new skateboard ramp area with fencing. The length is six feet more than the width of the area.

width = 24 feet

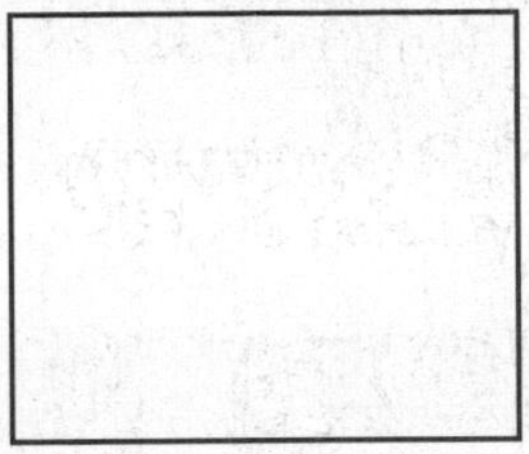

How much fencing will Jake need to go around the perimeter of his skateboard area?

○ **A** 96 feet

○ **B** 48 feet

○ **C** 108 feet

○ **D** 102 feet

3. Claire, Mia, and Mark each ride their horses at summer camp.

- Claire rides her horse **H** miles.

- Mia rides her horse 4 times as many miles as Claire does.

- Mark rides his horse 2 more miles than Claire does.

Use **H** to write an expression for the number of miles Mia rides her horse.

Use **H** to write an expression for the number of miles Mark rides his horse.

"A champion is someone who gets up when he can't." — Jack Dempsey, Athlete

/45

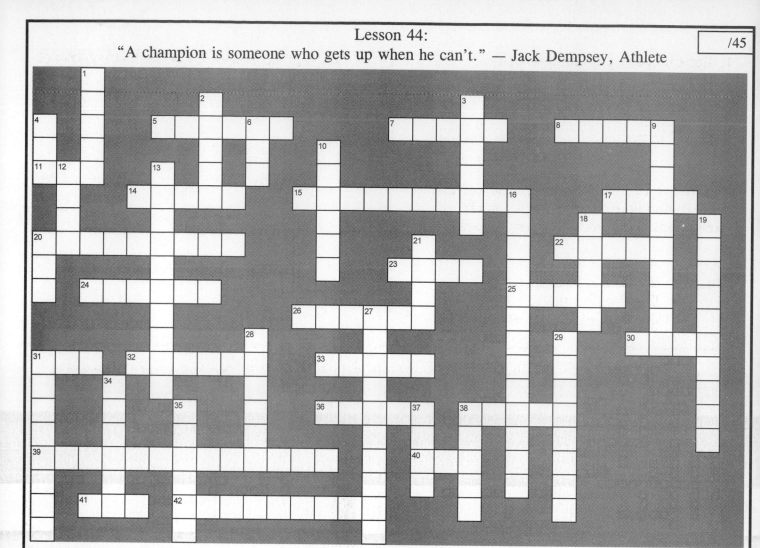

ACROSS

5 0.2 = N%

7 2 × N − 1 = 15

8 2 is a factor of 90. Right or wrong?

11 Estimate 76/25 − 31/15 to the nearest unit.

14 43 is composite. Right or wrong?

15 In 0.497, the digit 9 is in the ___ place.

17 The pink bag holds more cans than the blue bag. Which color bag probably has a greater volume?

20 Pattern: 3, 6, 5, 10, 9, 18, ___ .

22 Same chance of winning and losing. Chances of winning are N%.

23 The nth term of the pattern 4, 8, 12, 16, 20… can be expressed as ___ × n.

24 Surface area is measured in ___ units.

25 A circle has infinite lines of symmetry. Right or wrong?

26 Find factors with a ___ tree.

30 One unit to the right of -1 on a number line.

31 A recipe calls for 2/3 cup of sugar per batch. Bob is making three batches, how many cups?

32 Cubic units are used to measure this.

33 Right or wrong? The possible outcomes for two flips of a coin are: HH, HT, and TT.

36 In a fair game, the chance that either player will win is ___ .

38 A tool to measure weight.

39 Locating by observing the angle from two different points.

40 Surface area of 1 inch cube = N sq. in.

41 Surface area of 1 × 1 × 2 rectangular prism = N sq. units.

42 Quadrilateral whose name literally means "right angles".

DOWN

1 Greatest common factor of 12 and 15.

2 The opposite of -7.

3 Two lines intersect making a 150° angle. Other angle's measure?

4 # of radii in a diameter.

6 Distance between -1 and 9 on a number line.

9 A probability of 1 out of 4 = N%.

10 Area is measured in ___ units.

12 Number of diagonals in a hexagon.

13 Tool to measure angles.

16 A pyramid with a square base is aptly named this. (Two words.)

18 Mode is 8. Data is 6, 7, 8, and N.

19 Small unit of liquid measure, 1/8 cup. (Two words.)

20 Missing digit: 12.8 × 13.005 = 166.4__ _4

21 XXXOOOO. Ratio of × to O is 3 to ___ .

27 A certain quadrilateral has angles 10°, 50°, 100°, and N°.

28 A measure of how high something is.

29 A list of important events and the times they occurred.

31 The number halfway between 11 and 15.

34 Area is usually measured in ___ units.

35 Quadrilateral with four lines of symmetry.

37 One cubic yard (more less same) one cubic meter.

38 Temp. at 6 a.m. is 55°. Goes up 15° then down 10°. Temp. is now N°.

1. Look at the two rectangles below.

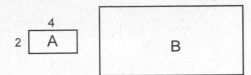

If each side of rectangle A is multiplied by 3 to make rectangle B, how does the area of rectangle B compare to the area of rectangle A?

- ○ **A**   B is 3 times as large
- ○ **B**   B is 2 times as large
- ○ **C**   B is 6 times as large
- ○ **D**   B is 9 times as large

2. Which group shows the prime factorization of the number 225?

- ○ **A**   5 x 45
- ○ **B**   3 x 3 x 5 x 5
- ○ **C**   25 + 200
- ○ **D**   (25 + 25 + 25 + 25) x 5

3. Simon is tracking the students in his class who ride their bikes to school each year. He has recorded the number of times they rode their bikes to school in the chart below.

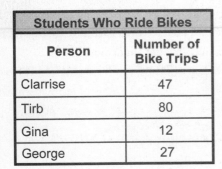

Students Who Ride Bikes	
Person	Number of Bike Trips
Clarrise	47
Tirb	80
Gina	12
George	27

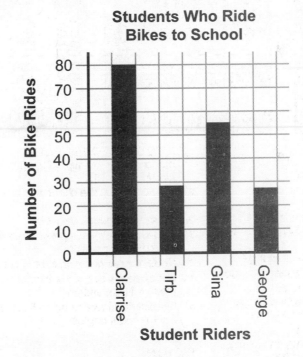

Simon made a graph of the information listed on the chart. Unfortunately, he was not a careful worker, and many of the pieces of information on the graph are incorrect. Which students have the incorrect number of volunteer hours recorded on the graph? Explain.

_____

_____

_____

_____

ACROSS

1 A paper circle is folded exactly in half. The crease is a line of ____ .

6 If 4 is 1 inch from 2 on a number line, what number is 1 inch to the right of 4?

7 The nth term of the pattern 4, 10, 16, 22… is ____ × n − 2.

8 Surface area of 1 × 1 × 3 rectangular prism = N sq. units.

12 Pattern: 20, 10, 12, 6, 8, 4, ____ , 3.

13 1% of 500.

14 Double and subtract 3. Pattern: 5, 7, 11, N.

17 Total possible outcomes for flipping two coins.

19 Right or wrong? The surface area of a box is greater than the area of one side of the box.

21 2:3 = 3/2. Right or wrong?

23 Missing digit: 8906.2204 ÷ 89.98 = 98.9___

25 The top and bottom of a box have area 6, while each of the 4 other sides have area 4. Surface area?

27 4 elephants weigh 3 tons. 12 elephants weigh N tons.

29 A tool to measure length.

31 A stop sign is this shape.

33 A probably of 1 out of 50 = N%.

34 Mean is 1. Data is 0, 0, 1, and N.

35 [] = 70 ÷ @. What is @ if [] = 7?

36 1/2 (more less same) 5/10.

37 Number of edges of a cube.

38 Two cubic inches (more less same) one cubic foot.

40 Distance between -10 and 10 on a number line.

41 I spent half my allowance plus $0.50 more. I have $1 left. Allowance = $N.

DOWN

1 1.42 + 4.58

2 Jorge Caballero, international soccer superstar, is exactly 2 meters tall. How tall is Jorge in centimeters?

3 30 × 0.5 − 5.0

4 Two lines intersect making a 165° angle. Other angle measure?

5 11/20 (more less same) 16/30.

9 1/4 = N%

10 A right triangle's short leg is 4, and its long leg is 6. What's the area?

11 3.5 units to the right of 4.5 on a number line.

13 16/5 + 19/20 is approximately what integer?

15 Right or wrong? 5.5 × 4 is an integer.

16 Right or wrong: 4.44 − one-half is about 4.

17 Diameter of circle = 10 inches. Radius of circle = N inches.

18 1/7 × 50 × 14 = 14/7 × N

20 How many of these are integers? 0, -1, 0.5, 1/2, 2.

22 The opposite of -1.

24 Start with 250. Do this 100 times: + 2, − 4.

26 A certain triangle has angles 87°, 91°, and N°.

28 Frank has 1384, Marty has 1359, Lloyd has 1278. Who has most?

30 15 clowns can fit into the VW, 19 clowns can fit into the phone booth. Volume of VW (more less same) volume of phone booth.

32 Each class gets 2.5 packs of paper. There are 8 classrooms, how many packs?

34 Half of 7: the operation is 1/2 ____ 7.

39 Compare: Mean of 8, 7 and 6 (more less same) mean of 7, 7 and 7.

1. The chart below show the number of sunny days in the city of Ferndale in select months last year.

Months	Number of Sunny Days
May	 ☀☀☀☀☀
July	 ☀☀☀
October	 ☀☀
January	 ☀☀☀☀☀

☀ = 6 days

How many sunny days were there during the month of May?

○ **A** 84   ○ **B** 27

○ **C** 30   ○ **D** 4.5

2. Look at the place value rods below.

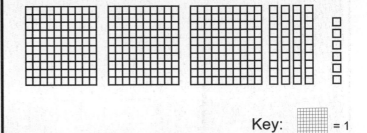

Key: ▦ = 1

What number is represented by the rods?

○ **A** 3.46

○ **B** 6.43

○ **C** 34.6

○ **D** 3460

3. Look at the factor tree below.

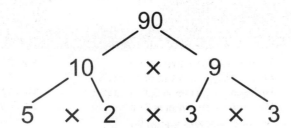

Draw a similar factor tree for 308 using multiplication.

Spelling List

acute	Euclid	nine	sixteen
addends	even	nineteen	sixty
a.m.	experiment	ninety	size
angles	exponent	obtuse	slide
arc	fact	octagon	sphere
area	factor	odd	square
average	Fahrenheit	one	square pyramid
backwards	fifteen	operations	stem and leaf
bar graph	fifty	ordered	straight
capacity	five	ordinal	surface area
Celsius	flip	parallel	symmetry
center	fluid ounce	parallelogram	tally
centimeter	forty	percent	temperature
certain	four	perpendicular	ten
circle	fourteen	place value	tenths
common	gallon	plane	terminating
composite	graph	p.m.	tessellation
cone	half	pound	thirteen
congruent	height	prime	thirty
coordinates	hexagon	prism	thousandths
cube	hundred	product	three
cubic	hundredth	protractor	tiling
cylinder	hundredths	pyramid	time line
decimal point	improper	Pythagoras	times
denominator	inch	quadrilateral	trapezoid
density	intersecting	quart	triangle
Descartes	isosceles	radii	triangulation
diagonal	kilogram	radius	turn
diameter	kilometer	ratio	twelve
divide	length	rectangle	twentieths
dividend	line	remainder	twenty
division	line graph	repeating	two
divisor	line segment	rhombus	variable
edges	liter	rotation	Venn
eight	meter	rounding	vertical
eighteen	metric system	ruler	volume
eighty	mile	scale	width
eleven	milliliter	scalene	yard
endpoint	millimeter	seven	zero
equal	mix	seventeen	
equally likely	mixed	seventy	
equilateral	multiples	similar	
equivalent	negative	six	

NUMBER SENSE

Types of Numbers

1, 2, 3, 4, 5, ...	Natural or Counting Numbers
0, 1, 2, 3, 4, 5, ...	Whole Numbers
... −3,−2,−1,0,1,2,3,...	Integers
...−4,− 2,0,2,4,6,8 ...	Even Numbers
...−3,−1,1,3,5,7,9 ...	Odd Numbers
1st, 2nd, 3rd, ...	Ordinal Numbers (tell what order)

Place Value

One hundred thirty four =

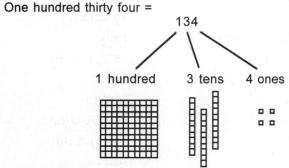

134

1 hundred   3 tens   4 ones

Numbers to the right of the decimal point tell fractions:

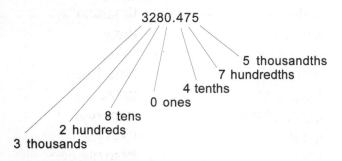

3280.475

5 thousandths
7 hundredths
4 tenths
0 ones
8 tens
2 hundreds
3 thousands

Fractions

Top number: Numerator. This tells how many parts.
Bottom number: Denominator. Tells size of each part.

Fraction Words

2 equal parts: Halves	3 equal parts: Thirds
4 equal parts: Fourths	5 equal parts: Fifths
6 equal parts: Sixths	7 equal parts: Sevenths
8 equal parts: Eighths	9 equal parts: Ninths, etc.

Types of Fractions

Mixed fraction: A whole number and a fraction together.
$3\frac{1}{2}$ = 3 and a half

Improper fraction: A fraction with a numerator greater than its denominator. $\frac{3}{2}$ is an improper fraction.

OPERATIONS

Addition 3 + 7 = 10   *The **sum** of 3 and 7 is 10.
3 and 7 are called the **addends**.*

Subtraction 9 − 4 = 5 *The **difference** between 9 and 4 is 5. 9 is the **subtrahend**, 4 is the **minuend**.*

Multiplication 4 × 5 = 20 *The **product** of 4 and 5 is 20.
4 is the **multiplier**. 5 is the **multiplicand**.*
Multiplication is **repeated addition**: 4 × 5 means add 4 five times, or 4 + 4 + 4 + 4 + 4 = 20. 4 × 5 can also mean add 5 four times, or 5 + 5 + 5 + 5 = 20.

Division 12 ÷ 2 = 6   *The **quotient** of 12 and 2 is 6.
12 is the **dividend**. 2 is the **divisor**.*
Division can mean **repeated subtraction**: 20 ÷ 4 = 5 because you can subtract 4 from 20 five times.

Fact Family: A group of numbers related by an operation, like 3, 5, 8, since 3 + 5 = 8, 8 − 5 = 3, etc.

Commutative property: It doesn't matter in which order you add or multiply:
2 + 3 = 3 + 2 and 3 × 7 = 7 × 3.
• It <u>does</u> matter in which order you subtract or divide!
5 − 2 ≠ 2 − 5, and 12 ÷ 3 ≠ 3 ÷ 12 !

The **associative property** of addition says that a group of numbers may be added in any pairs:
(1+2) + 3 = 1 + (2 + 3)
• Multiplication is also **associative**:
(2 × 3) × 5 = 2 × (3 × 5)

Factors, Primes, and Composites

Parts that a number can be evenly divided by are called **divisors**. *For example: 8 can be evenly divided by 1, 2, 4, and 8, so 1, 2, 4, and 8 are divisors of 8.*

Divisors are also called **factors**.

Examples: *Factors of 10: 1, 2, 5, 10
Factors of 11: 1, 11
Factors of 12: 1, 2, 3, 4, 6, 12*

Every number (greater than one) has at least 2 factors. One of the factors is 1, another is the number itself.

If a number's only factors are 1 and itself, that number is **prime**. *For example, 13 has no other factors besides 1 and 13, so 13 is prime.*
Prime numbers: 2, 3, 5, 7, 11, 13, 17, 19, 23, 29, ...

If a number has more than just 2 factors, it is called **composite**. *For example, 6 is composite, because it has more than 2 factors.*
Composite numbers: 4, 6, 8, 9, 10, 12, 14, 15, 16, 18...

The number 1 is neither prime nor composite.

MEASUREMENT

Length

one inch: [   ]

← 1 inch →

12 inches =   1 foot
3 feet =   1 yard
5280 feet =   1 mile

Length can be measured with a **ruler**.

Metric System

one centimeter: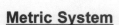
1 cm

one square centimeter: [ ]

$1 cm^2$

one cubic centimeter:

$1 cm^3$

10 millimeters =   1 centimeter
100 centimeters =   1 meter
1000 meters =   1 kilometer

1 cubic centimeter = 1 milliliter
1000 milliliters = 1 liter
1 liter = a little more than 1 quart

Volume or Capacity

Volume: How *much* something holds (2 liters, 5 cubic feet, etc.)
Capacity: How *many* something holds (4 grapefruit, 20 kids, etc.)

2 cups =   1 pint
2 pints =   1 quart
4 quarts =   1 gallon

8 ounces = 1 cup
4 cups = 1 quart

Volume can be measured with
measuring cups.

Standard Units

Units of length (linear units):   inches, feet, yards, miles, millimeters, centimeters, meters, kilometers, etc.
Units of area (square units):   square inches, square feet, square yards, square miles, square meters, etc.
Units of volume (cubic units):   cubic inches, cubic feet, cubic yards, cubic centimeters, cubic meters, etc.

Weight & Mass

16 ounces = 1 pound   1000 milligrams = 1 gram
2000 pounds = 1 ton   1000 grams = 1 kilogram

Weight can be measured with a **scale** or a **balance**.

Time

60 seconds = 1 minute   A **calendar** shows months and days.
60 minutes = 1 hour   A **clock** tells what time it is.
24 hours = 1 day   A **timer** measures time.
7 days = 1 week   A **timeline** shows important dates in history.
2 weeks = 1 fortnight
365 days = 1 year   2:00 A.M. = **midnight**
10 years = 1 decade   12:00 P.M. = **noon**
100 years = 1 century   **A.M.** means before noon.
1000 years = 1 millennium   **P.M.** means after noon.

GEOMETRY

Points, Lines, Planes

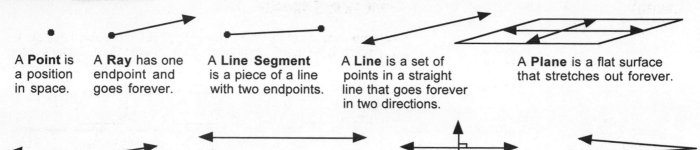

A **Point** is a position in space.

A **Ray** has one endpoint and goes forever.

A **Line Segment** is a piece of a line with two endpoints.

A **Line** is a set of points in a straight line that goes forever in two directions.

A **Plane** is a flat surface that stretches out forever.

Intersecting lines cross.

Parallel lines never meet.

Perpendicular lines meet at a right angle.

Two rays with the same endpoint is called an **angle.**

Angles

Acute angle: smaller than a right angle; less than 90°
Right angle: like a square corner; = 90°
Obtuse angle: greater than a right angle; more than 90°

Complementary: Two angles which make 90°
Supplementary: Two angles which make 180° (a straight line)

Triangles (Polygons with 3 sides)

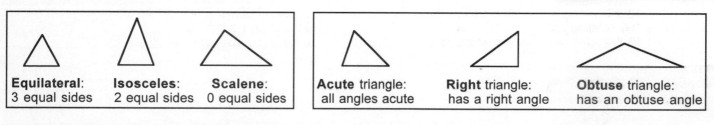

Equilateral: 3 equal sides

Isosceles: 2 equal sides

Scalene: 0 equal sides

Acute triangle: all angles acute

Right triangle: has a right angle

Obtuse triangle: has an obtuse angle

Quadrilaterals (Polygons with 4 sides)

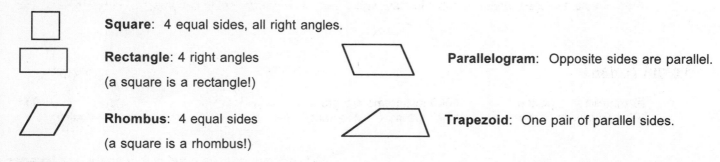

Square: 4 equal sides, all right angles.

Rectangle: 4 right angles

(a square is a rectangle!)

Parallelogram: Opposite sides are parallel.

Rhombus: 4 equal sides

(a square is a rhombus!)

Trapezoid: One pair of parallel sides.

Circles

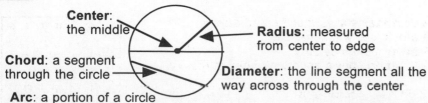

Center: the middle

Radius: measured from center to edge

Chord: a segment through the circle

Diameter: the line segment all the way across through the center

Arc: a portion of a circle

Compass: a tool to draw circles
Circumference: the measure all the way around the circle.
$$C = \pi d = 2 \pi r$$
Area of a circle $= \pi r^2$

111

Polygons

Polygons are closed shapes made with straight edges.
Regular polygons have all sides the same length and all angles the same measure.

# sides:	3	4	5	6	7	8	9	10
name:	**triangle**	**quadrilateral**	**pentagon**	**hexagon**	**heptagon** (or septagon)	**octagon**	**nonagon** (or enneagon)	**decagon**

congruent = same size and shape   **similar** = same shape, same ratio between measures

3D Shapes

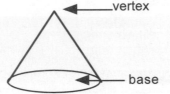

Cone:
one circular base
one vertex

vertex

base

Pyramid:
one polygon base
one vertex

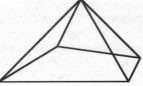

The volume of a cone or a pyramid = 1/3 area of base × height

Prism:
two parallel bases
which are polygons

Cylinder:
two parallel bases
which are circles

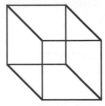

bases

Vertices are corners.
Faces are flat surfaces.
Sides of faces are **edges.**

The volume of a cylinder or a prism = area of base × height

Cube:
6 square faces

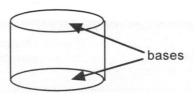

Sphere:
perfectly circular
ball shape

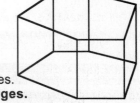

Volume = side length cubed

Volume = 4/3 π r^3 Surface area = 4 π r^2

Transformations

Slide or **Translation**

Flip or **Reflection** or **Mirror Image**

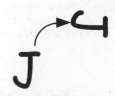

Turn or **Rotation**

A **Line of Symmetry**
divides a shape into
two mirror image halves.

112

DATA ANALYSIS AND PROBABILITY

Graphs

Line Graph:
Shows how data
changes over time.

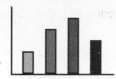

Bar Graph:
The taller the bar, the
greater the amount.

	a	b
1	4	5
2	9	11
3	6	3.14

Table: A chart with rows and columns.
Spreadsheet: A program on a computer that
arranges data in a table or an array.
Array: A way to organize numbers in a grid.

Data

Tally marks: A record of data, made by making small marks. ＨＨＴ ＨＨＴ ＩＩ

Survey: Questions asked to a group of people to gather information.

Range: The difference between the greatest and least numbers in a set of data. The range of {2,6,7} is 5.
Mode: The item that shows up most in a list of data. In {1,2,5,7,7,7}, the mode is 7.
Median: The number that shows up in the middle of a set of <u>ordered</u> data. If there are two middle numbers,
then the median is the mean of these two numbers.   In {3,6,9,10,10}, the median is 9.
In {1,2,3,4} the median is 2.5.
Mean: The sum of a set of data divided by the number of elements in the set of data.
The mean of {1,5,6} is 4, since (1+5+6) / 3 = 4.

Probability

Impossible: An event that will never happen.

Not Likely, or **Unlikely**: Something that probably won't happen.

Likely: Something that probably will happen.

Certain: An event that will definitely happen.

Experiment: A trial where you don't know the outcome.

Fair: A game where all players have an equal chance.

Independent: Two events whose outcomes do not influence one another.

ALGEBRA

Symbols

= equals sign   *3 plus 2 equals 5... 3 + 2 = 5*
> greater than   *7 is greater than 5... 7 > 5*
< less than   *99 is less than 100... 99 < 100*

Patterns

Skip counting: Counting by multiples of a number.
Skip counting by 5 is: 5, 10, 15, 20, 25, 30, ...

Lesson 1: "All glory comes from daring to begin."
Eugene F. Ware, Author

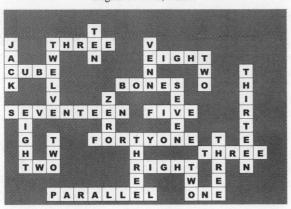

Lesson 2: "Do not be timid about your actions. All life is an experiment."
Ralph Waldo Emerson, Philosopher

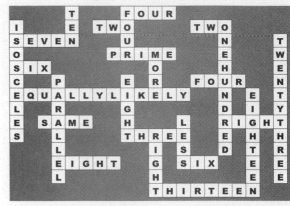

Lesson 3: "Good enough never is."
Debbi Field, Founder of Mrs. Field's Cookies

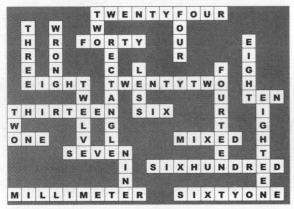

Lesson 4: "If you stand at all, stand tall."
King James I of England

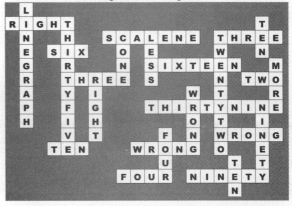

Lesson 6: "Problems are only opportunities in work clothes."
Henry Kaiser, Builder

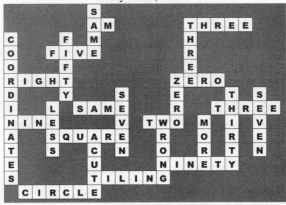

Lesson 7: "There's a better way to do it. Find it!"
Thomas Edison, Inventor

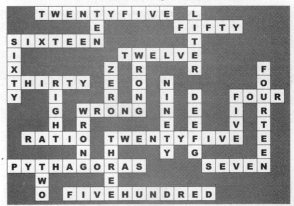

Lesson 8: "What would you attempt if you knew you could not fail?"
Dr. Robert Schuller, Minister

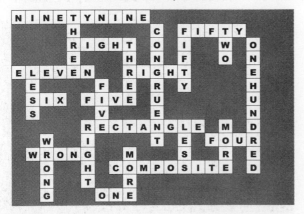

Lesson 9: "One of the secrets of life is to make stepping stones out of stumbling blocks."
Jack Penn, Author

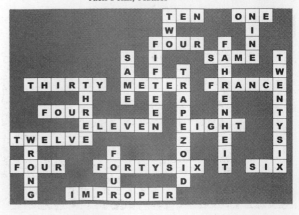

114

Lesson 11: "Light tomorrow with today!"
Elizabeth Barrett Browning, Author

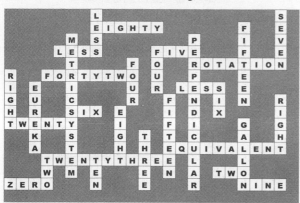

Lesson 12: "The things that count most in life are usually the things that cannot be counted."
Bernard Meltzer, Attorney

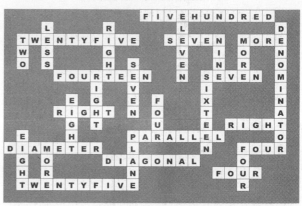

Lesson 13: "The times change and we change with them."
John Owen, Poet

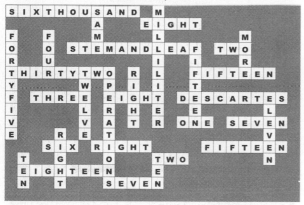

Lesson 14: "Let no one ever come to you without leaving better and happier."
Mother Theresa, Missionary

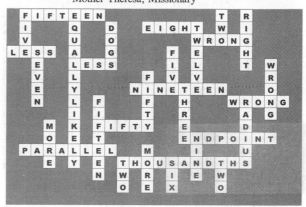

Lesson 16: "Advice: it's more fun to give than to receive."
Malcolm Forbes, Business Leader

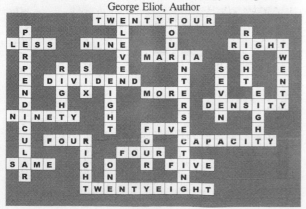

Lesson 17: "Well done is better than well said."
Benjamin Franklin, Statesman

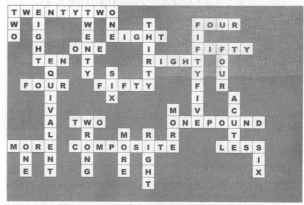

Lesson 18: "It is never too late to become what you might have been."
George Eliot, Author

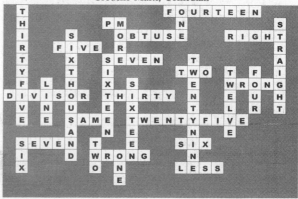

Lesson 19: "Before I speak, I have something important to say."
Groucho Marx, Comedian

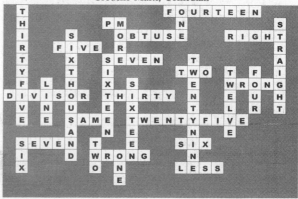

115

Lesson 21: "Obstacles are things a person sees when he takes his eyes off the goal."
E. Joseph Cossman, Salesman

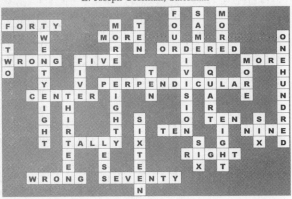

Lesson 22: "Nothing lasts forever, not even your troubles."
Arnold H. Glasgow, Psychologist

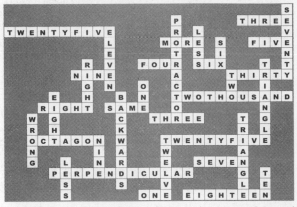

Lesson 23: "If opportunity doesn't knock, build a door."
Milton Berle, Comedian

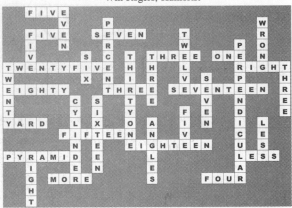

Lesson 24: "To be upset over what you don't have is to waste what you do have."
Ken S. Keyes, Jr., Author

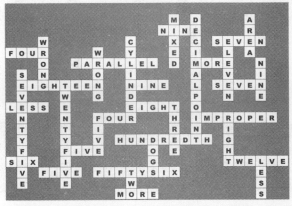

Lesson 26: "Even if you're on the right track, you'll get run over if you just sit there."
Will Rogers, Humorist

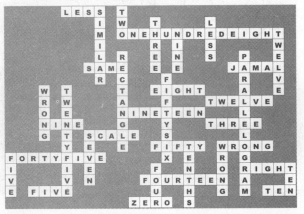

Lesson 27: "The man who makes no mistakes does not usually make anything."
W.C. Magee, Bishop

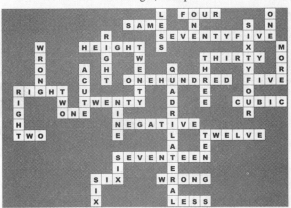

Lesson 28: "Imagination is more important than knowledge."
Einstein, Physicist

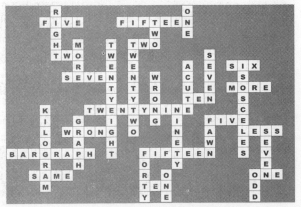

Lesson 29: "A friend is a present you give yourself."
Robert Louis Stevenson, Author

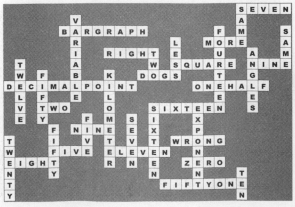

116

Lesson 31: "In order to achieve anything, you must be brave enough to fail."
Kirk Douglas, Actor

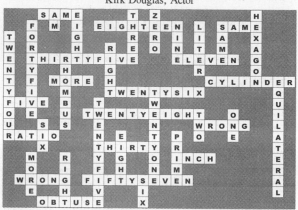

Lesson 32: "Never mistake motion for action."
Ernest Hemingway, Author

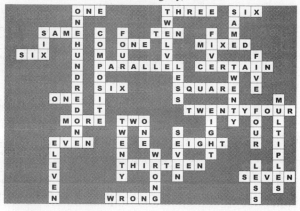

Lesson 33: "Whenever I don't have the answer to something, I find someone who does."
Walt Disney, Cartoonist

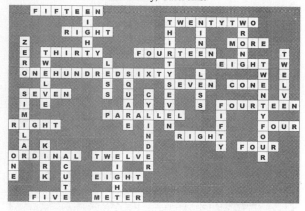

Lesson 34: "Things turn out best for the people who make the best of the way things turn out."
Art Linkletter, Personality

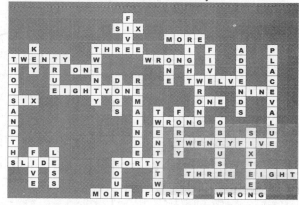

Lesson 36: "A book is like a garden carried in the pocket."
Chinese Proverb

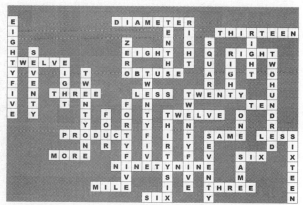

Lesson 37: "We cannot become what we need to be by remaining what we are."
Max de Pree, Author

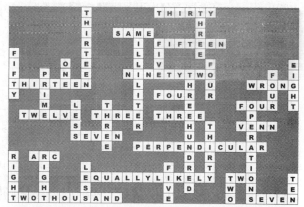

Lesson 38: "What the heart knows today the head will understand tomorrow."
James Stephens, Author

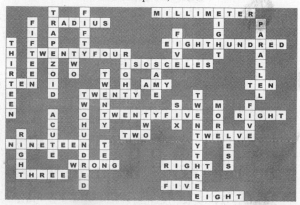

Lesson 39: "People don't really care how much you know until they know how much you care."
Mike McKnight, Musician

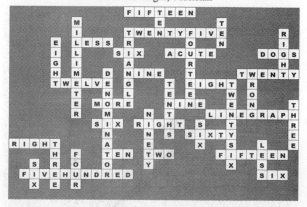

117

Lesson 41: "Not knowing when the dawn will come, I open every door."
Emily Dickinson, Poet

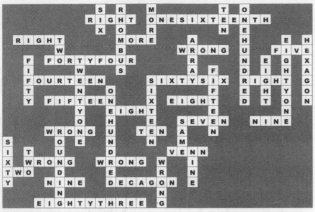

Lesson 42: "One person can make a difference, and every person should tr[...]"
John F. Kennedy, President

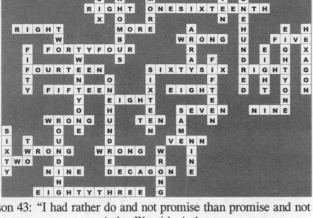

Lesson 43: "I had rather do and not promise than promise and not do."
Arthur Warwick, Author

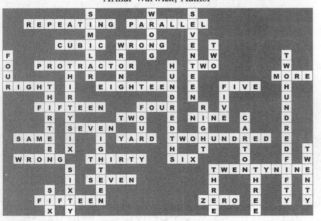

Lesson 44: "A champion is someone who gets up when he can't."
Jack Dempsey, Athlete

Application Page Answer Keys

Lesson 1:	Lesson 2:	Lesson 3:	Lesson 4:	Lesson 6:	Lesson 7:
1: A 2: D	1: C 2: D	1: C 2: D	1: B 2: A	1: D 2: B	1: A 2: D

Lesson 8:	Lesson 9:	Lesson 11:	Lesson 12:	Lesson 13:	Lesson 14:
1: A 2: D	1: B 2: C	1: A 2: D	1: B 2: B	1: B 2: D	1: B 2: A

Lesson 16:	Lesson 17:	Lesson 18:	Lesson 19:	Lesson 21:	Lesson 22:
1: C 2: A	1: A 2: D	1: A 2: A	1: C 2: B	1: D 2: D	1: D 2: A

Lesson 23:	Lesson 24:	Lesson 26:	Lesson 27:	Lesson 28:	Lesson 29:
1: B 2: D	1: B 2: D	1: C 2: D	1: C 2: D	1: C 2: C	1: A 2: A

Lesson 31:	Lesson 32:	Lesson 33:	Lesson 34:	Lesson 36:	Lesson 37:
1: C 2: B	1: B 2: C	1: B 2: D	1: D 2: A	1: C 2: B	1: A 2: A

Lesson 38:	Lesson 39:	Lesson 41:	Lesson 42:	Lesson 43:	Lesson 44:
1: B 2: C	1: C 2: A	1: C 2: D	1: B 2: D	1: B 2: C	1: D 2: B

Lesson 5: Assessment 1

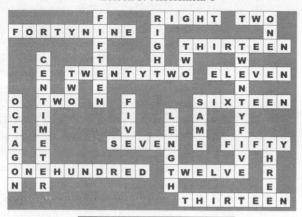

Application Answers:
1: C   2: C

Lesson 10: Assessment 2

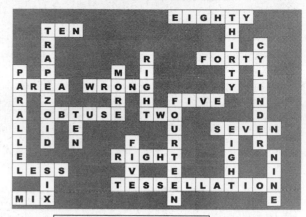

Application Answers:
1: A   2: C

Lesson 15: Assessment 3

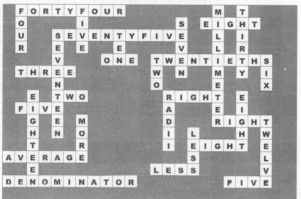

Application Answers:
1: B   2: C

Lesson 20: Assessment 4

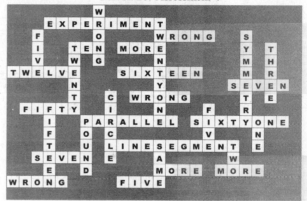

Application Answers:
1: A   2: B

Lesson 25: Assessment 5

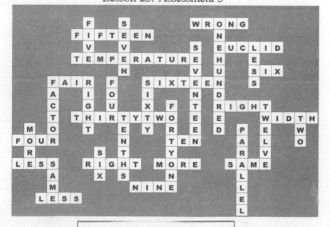

Application Answers:
1: B   2: C

Lesson 30: Assessment 6

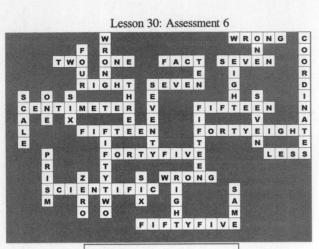

Application Answers:
1: D   2: D

Lesson 35: Assessment 7

Application Answers:
1: C   2: B

Lesson 40: Assessment 8

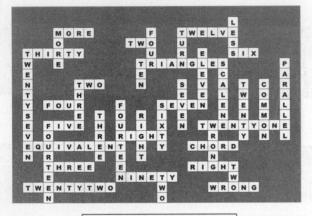

Application Answers:
1: D   2: A

Lesson 45: Assessment 9

Application Answers:
1: B   2: A

À ma sœur, Erin.
Mary Shaw

À ma mère, June,
dont les mots d'encouragement
et l'attitude positive
ont été ma source d'inspiration.
Chuck Temple Junior

Brady Brady
et le gardien disparu

Mary Shaw

Illustrations de Chuck Temple

Texte français de Jocelyne Henri

Éditions
SCHOLASTIC

Catalogage avant publication de Bibliothèque
et Archives Canada

Shaw, Mary, 1965-
[Brady Brady and the runaway goalie. Français]
Brady Brady et le gardien disparu

Traduction de : Brady Brady and the runaway goalie.
Pour enfants de 4 à 8 ans.

ISBN-13 978-0-439-98693-9
ISBN-10 0-439-98693-1

I. Temple, Chuck, 1962- . II. Henri, Jocelyne. III. Titre.

PS8587.H38B7314 2001   jC843'.6   C2001-900944-5

PZ23.S52Bra 2001

Édition publiée par les Éditions Scholastic,
604, rue King Ouest, Toronto (Ontario) M5V 1E1.

6 5 4 3 2   Imprimé au Canada   07 08 09 10 11

Brady aime l'hiver. Il aime l'hiver parce qu'il aime le hockey. Il ne pense à rien d'autre qu'au hockey. Il y pense tellement qu'il faut l'appeler deux fois pour attirer son attention. Sa famille est en train de devenir *folle!*

— Brady, Brady! As-tu fait ton lit?

— Brady, Brady! Champion veut sortir.

— Brady, Brady! Tu renverses ton lait!

À la longue, sa famille a fini par l'appeler Brady Brady.
C'est plus facile de cette façon.

Brady fait partie d'une équipe appelée les Ricochons. L'aréna où ils jouent est à un coin de rue de chez Brady. Ce n'est pas loin, mais Brady part toujours tôt pour être le premier arrivé.

Un samedi matin, les Ricochons doivent jouer contre une équipe de durs appelée les Dragons. Les Dragons n'ont jamais été vaincus. En se rendant à l'aréna, Brady se sent agité et un peu nerveux.

En entrant, Brady salue Charlie, son ami. Charlie est le gardien de but des Ricochons et le garçon le plus intelligent que Brady connaisse. Il aide souvent Brady à faire ses devoirs de mathématiques.

Avant chaque match, Charlie donne aussi un coup de main au casse-croûte de l'aréna. Il dit que grignoter du maïs soufflé l'empêche de penser aux rondelles lancées vers son filet et le débarrasse de ses papillons à l'estomac.

Brady remarque que Charlie a l'air plus nerveux aujourd'hui.

— On se revoit dans le vestiaire des joueurs, Charlie, lui dit Brady, en passant devant le casse-croûte.

— D'accord, Brady Brady, marmonne Charlie, sans regarder son ami.

Avant un match, il y a habituellement beaucoup de bavardage, mais aujourd'hui le vestiaire des Ricochons est presque silencieux. La mauvaise réputation des Dragons inquiète les Ricochons.

Quand tous les joueurs sont habillés,
ils se rassemblent au centre de la pièce pour lancer leur cri de ralliement.
Mais ils ne sont pas aussi bruyants qu'à l'habitude.

**« On est les plus forts,
On est les meilleurs,
On va les avoir…**

… Y a quelque chose qui cloche! »

Ils regardent autour d'eux… et voient l'équipement du gardien dans un tas. Charlie a disparu!

— Brady Brady! Essaie de le retrouver, dit l'entraîneur.

Brady sort à toute vitesse. Une seconde plus tard, il revient avec une note qu'il a trouvée sur la porte. Il la lit à haute voix.

— Oh, non! grogne l'entraîneur.
Nous ne pouvons pas jouer sans notre gardien!

Des joueurs s'assoient et commencent à délacer leurs patins.

— Attendez! crie Brady. Mais nous avons un gardien.
Il faut simplement le retrouver.

Ils regardent derrière la machine
à maïs soufflé du casse-croûte.
Pas de Charlie.

Ils regardent sous les gradins.
Il y a de la gomme collée sous les sièges.
Mais pas de Charlie.

Ils regardent partout, même dans les toilettes des filles.
Toujours pas de Charlie.

Enfin, ils regardent dans le garage.
Charlie est là, assis sur la surfaceuse.

— Descends, Charlie. Nous avons besoin de toi, le supplie Brady.
— Je ne peux pas affronter les Dragons, Brady Brady, gémit
Charlie. J'ai peur.
— Tu n'as pas à les affronter tout seul, mon gars, lui dit
l'entraîneur. Nous sommes les Ricochons. Nous les
affronterons en équipe.
— Nous sommes tous un peu nerveux, Charlie,
ajoute Brady. Mais tu peux être plus malin que
les Dragons n'importe quand.

Les joueurs des Ricochons lancent leur cri de
ralliement. Cette fois, ils sont aussi bruyants
et aussi fiers que d'habitude.

« On est les plus forts,
On est les meilleurs,
Notre gardien s'appelle Charlie,
On est ses amis! »

Charlie descend de la surfaceuse.

Sur la patinoire, les Ricochons s'alignent devant les Dragons.
Brady entend Charlie claquer des dents derrière son masque.

L'arbitre fait la mise au jeu et le match commence.
Les Dragons plaquent leurs adversaires et leur donnent des coups de bâton.
Ils jouent comme des brutes, mais les Ricochons n'abandonnent pas.
Toute l'équipe sait qu'elle doit faire de gros efforts pour aider Charlie…
surtout que leur gardien a les yeux fermés la plupart du temps.

À la fin de la troisième période, le score est toujours zéro à zéro.
Durant la période supplémentaire, personne ne compte.
Il ne reste alors qu'une solution : *la fusillade!*

Charlie tente de quitter la patinoire, mais ses coéquipiers
le ramènent à son filet.

— Allez, Charlie, tu es capable, lui dit Brady, en lui donnant
une tape dans le dos. Tu peux être le meilleur quand tu veux!

Les Ricochons sont les premiers à tirer,
et c'est Brady qui est choisi. Partant du centre de la glace,
il fonce à toute vitesse vers le gardien adverse,
la rondelle sur la lame de son bâton.
Il entend les encouragements de ses coéquipiers.

Brady tire en direction du filet. *Ping!* La rondelle frappe
la barre transversale… et retombe dans le filet!

La foule se déchaîne, sauf les partisans des Dragons, bien entendu.

C'est maintenant au tour des Dragons.
Brady regarde Charlie et lui fait signe que tout va bien.

— Rappelle-toi, Charlie, tu peux être le meilleur quand tu veux!

Le joueur des Dragons commence son attaque.
La sueur coule sur le visage de Charlie, mais il ne ferme pas les yeux.
Il se met plutôt à réfléchir.

— La vitesse de la rondelle… fois l'arc de la rondelle…
marmonne-t-il, ce qui signifie… qu'elle devrait arriver… *exactement*…

Charlie tient encore la rondelle quand ses coéquipiers
le soulèvent sur leurs épaules.

— Je *savais* que tu y arriverais! dit fièrement Brady à son ami.

Son ami, le super gardien *retrouvé* des Ricochons.

... ICI!

Flac!

La rondelle se loge
dans le gant tendu
de Charlie.

— *Hourra pour notre gardien!*
s'écrient les Ricochons.

Les joueurs sautent par-dessus la bande pour rejoindre Charlie,
qui n'a pas encore bougé.